Sorry We Missed You

Written by Paul Laverty
Directed by Ken Loach
Produced by Rebecca O'Brien

First published in 2019 by Route
PO Box 167, Pontefract, WF8 4WW
info@route-online.com
www.route-online.com

In association with Sixteen Films
2nd Floor, 187 Wardour Street, London, W1F 8ZB

ISBN: 978-1-901927-79-5

Cover design:
GOLDEN
From artwork supplied by Entertainment One UK Ltd

A catalogue for this book is available from the British Library

Printed in EU by Pulsio SARL

Contents

Paul Laverty
Writer

I found the notebooks. One page had a question. 'What if… we have a family that sleeps in the same house; they are only a few feet away from each other for hours on end. But they hardly see each other at all. At least during the daylight hours.'

The Turner family felt like they lived a safe distance from Daniel Blake, although in the same city.

I remember sitting beside Ken some 20 years ago as we gave interviews. He said, 'There's something of an iceberg about a film; you might not see it all, but you sense its weight under the surface.' It has always stuck with me.

The endless doodles, nonsenses, and possibilities in notebooks before the writing are for me the presence under the surface; sometimes they will never reach the script never mind celluloid, but somehow they are there, even if we eventually work against them, or contradict them.

I found the following snippets as characters, and the bones of a story emerged through the mist. And they changed through time.

Liza Jane, age 10 or 11. Sometimes she feels like David Attenborough looking for signs of human existence in the stillness of the house. She loves nature programmes and has a flying imagination that keeps her company in the long hours she is by herself. She knows her family are out there somewhere… signs of half-eaten food (dirty plates from breakfast) cast-off skin (sweaty t-shirts). Both Mum and Dad have to go out hunting, a long and laborious task that leaves them, just like the big cats, often grumpy, empty-handed, and licking their wounds…

Seb, aged 15, has his head inside a hoodie, even when he's not wearing it. His secret wish is invisibility. Give me peace, no sermons, just let me work things out for myself. Seb and Liza Jane are close and most evenings they eat together alone watching videos. Some make them laugh, but some leave them empty.

Seb is much more insightful than he appears. He has his sister's brains – they are both sharp, but he is determined to hide it. It gives him deep satisfaction to see how this riles his father Ricky; he knows the buttons to press and often does. He can't resist the impulse and doesn't know why. At least when his dad is shouting at him, he's present. A few years back they laughed a lot. He won't admit it, but he misses his quiet chats with his mother Abby who seems to sense what he feels without ever asking.

Seb is consumed by his passion, graffiti, after flirting with parkour. As he heads into the night he can burn off anger fizzing inside. He feels free, and wild, everything his father isn't. He thinks in images, not words.

How does Seb feel when one of his closest mates disappears out of his life?

Ricky and Abby remember that first night they met in a rave in Morecambe. Instant connection. Ease.

Northern Rock Building Society: how the financial crisis ended their hopes of owning their own home. If Northern Rock had collapsed just one month later, it would have been a life-changer. Abby cried her eyes out the entire night their mortgage fell through. That house was theirs, and her child would be born there. But it wasn't to be. It still seems out of reach as moving from one rented house to another has gnawed away at her sense of security. Some people dream of winning the lottery. Abby dreams of decorating a house one day in her favourite colours. Her choice, not a landlord's. And never moving again.

Ricky; a hungry, searching quality to him; he has never really found his spot. His last job was the last straw; an assistant landscaper… he worked at twice the speed of his fellow worker who got promoted to supervisor. That's fucking it! Told them to stick it. He's an impulsive man who takes pride in being a grafter, and never having taken a penny off the State. Just as well.

If he was forced to the Job Centre some security guard would be likely to get a punch in the gub.

In a rattling old van full of labourers dozing off after a day's work, Ricky would imagine Seb at uni. The first in his family, followed by Liza Jane, top of her class. They won't have hands like mine.

Abby has always admired Ricky's independent streak. There was always a whiff of danger behind the banter; she could sense his loyalty to her. But as time moved on, and life impinged, she could feel annoyance in her gut; sometimes he doesn't notice what is going on in front of his eyes. Misses the signs. Leaps before he thinks.

Compassion runs through Abby's veins as much as blood. Where did that big heart come from? Even the most demented of her patients can sense it; how else could they comb her hair? (The secret to her working life is revealed in a flash of anger at a bus stop to a total stranger.)

Over these past months she has been haunted by a dream.

She often feels she spends more time in other people's houses than her own. Is that it, for the rest of her working life? Will it always feel so tight, so little choice? How she loved her little car, how she misses it. Not just for herself; she feels that the old people she works with have the right to see the same face for their last days. For some of them she is the single most important person in their lives. She tries not to miss their funerals when the time comes. But how she misses time at home with her kids.

She can't bear swearing; conflict reminds her of her own childhood.

Another character emerged. The heavy-duty van with more comfort, more load capacity than competitors.

The van gets the job done.

Ricky can feel his spirits rise. No more constipated bosses, no more lazy slackers to slow him down. He will work like a dog, outperform; he'll be on that road with his van – a freelancer, a warrior.

William Blake warned us of 'the mind-forg'd manacles'.

The gobbledygook contractual language of the new workplace that Ricky has to sign.

The scanner; in the palm of a hand... a mind-blowing piece of sophistication and brilliance from some of the sharpest brains in the world. For what purpose?

Enough.

In other words, a story is one big dumping ground; we have to sieve it, interrogate it, challenge it, tie it all up and make connections, both inside the house and outside that front door.

We do that at every stage of the film, from our first daydreams over a coffee, to layers of talent coming on board and making it their own. From a glint in a child's eye, to the faintest hint of minimalist sound.

It always feels like one long wrestling match with a giant slippery eel.

The Turners. Only four of them, but each family is an ocean of possibilities.

It all feels very fragile, and at the end of the day it is a bet, never a thesis.

Sorry We Missed You

Screenplay

1. TITLES ON BLACK

TWO MALE VOICES: [Both have wit and vitality. Ricky, with a Manchester accent, has an unexpected quality to him. Direct. Maloney, a depot supervisor, with a Geordie accent, is middle-aged, streetwise, been round many blocks and as hard as nails.]

RICKY

You name it, I've done it... everything on a building site... groundworking, marking out and digging the trenches for foundations... concreting, layering and smoothing for floors and beams... labourer, brickie, slabbing, driving a dumper truck, digging holes, even graves... believe me, everything...

MALONEY

So why did you give it up?

RICKY

Always some prat nipping your brain... balls frozen off five storeys up... all takes its toll...

MALONEY

What about the landscaping job?

RICKY

Loved it, out and about... I'm a grafter... but carrying too many lazy bastards in my

squad... [sigh] It's now or never... I want to
be my own man, my own boss... fucking sick
to the back teeth of working for people...
done my head in.

MALONEY

Have you ever been on the dole?

RICKY

Starve first... not one day.

MALONEY

Music to my ears Ricky... Henry was right,
you are a trooper. Now, let's get things
clear from the start, you don't get 'hired'
here... you come 'onboard'... Yes, we call it
'onboarding'... you don't work for us, you
work with us, you don't drive for us, you
perform services, no employment contracts,
no performance targets, you meet delivery
standards, no wages... but fees... have you
got that?

RICKY

Sounds good to me.

MALONEY

No clocking in, you become available...
you sign up with us, you become an Owner
Driver Franchisee... how does that sound?

RICKY

Franchisee... sounds a bit fancy.

MALONEY

Master of your own destiny… it sorts out the
fucking losers from the warriors… are you up
for that?

Now we see Ricky for the first time. Early forties. He holds
Maloney's eye, something immediate about him.

RICKY

I've been waiting for this for far too long…

MALONEY

The only other big question before signing the
franchise… do you bring your own van, or
hire with us?

RICKY

I'll have a word with Henry…

MALONEY

Well, let me know… like everything else
here… it's your choice…

2. VAN DEALERSHIP, NEWCASTLE

Two small figures in the distance are dwarfed by lines of dozens
of white vans of all sorts.

Ricky walks alongside his mate Henry, who wears a military-
style type jacket and cap. He's an intense man, who takes life
seriously.

HENRY

You've got to think long term Ricky. If too
much mileage, battered to hell… if you lose
a day at work… you pay the replacement…

whack! Two hundred quid, right there in the
nuts! So go for one in good nick…

They pass a VW Crafter van, in good condition, for £13,950.

HENRY (CONT'D)
I went for this… bigger… get the outsize
parcels, bonuses, flexibility, but still small
enough so no limits on your driving… can do
twenty-four hour straight if you need to…

RICKY
Seventeen fucking grand! Abby will have
kittens… still paying off the last loan.

HENRY
Do the maths… you pay about four hundred
quid a month for this … but if you hire from
the company that's sixty-five quid a day! A
day! Tough at the beginning… but in twelve
months I'll have four vans running… maybe a
few Polish lads who won't piss around… that
could be you… but there is a big if… [Ricky
looks round at him] you need a thousand
pound deposit for your own van…

RICKY
No chance…

HENRY
Find it! Or you'll be back wiping a boss's arse
for the rest of your life.

3. HOME, NEWCASTLE – NIGHT

An ordinary street, off a busy main road. Terraced Tyneside flats. Most are rented. Many are shabby and faded, but not totally run down. Several signs for rent pepper the street.

A modest little car, neat and distinctive, pulls up. Abby, early forties, dressed in a carer's uniform and carrying a bag with her equipment, gets out, and heads towards her home. It is the end of a long day and she is exhausted. She makes her way to a front door that could do with a lick of paint.

INSIDE: By the front door there is a simple shelf on the wall where everyone leaves their keys. Sounds of keys and the door opening. Abby lays her car key and house keys, with a key ring of a bear, on the shelf to join the other two sets there belonging to Ricky and Liza Jane. [The process of keys in and out on the shelf on entering and leaving the house is a family ritual for them all. Each key ring has a distinct animal.]

Abby climbs the stairs to their flat above. Noise of a bedroom door opening. Liza Jane appears before Abby in her pyjamas and gives her mum a big hug.

> ABBY
> Liza Jane... it's after ten darling... should be dreaming...

> LIZA JANE
> Couldn't sleep...

Abby hugs her tight.

> ABBY
> Sorry sweetheart, got held up with the 'tuck-ins'.

> LIZA JANE
> Old Joe?

ABBY

Found him in the pub! Go... to bed!

LIZA JANE

Any funny stories?

ABBY

Tomorrow... I'll get back earlier... I promise.

LATER: IN THE KITCHEN AND LIVING ROOM:
Ricky makes a cup of tea while Abby, in the adjoining living
room, studies the shiny brochure for the van. There are also
miscellaneous pieces of paper with columns of figures and bills
laid out before them both as they consider their options.

ABBY (CONT'D)

It's £416 a month! Can you not use a
company van?

RICKY

They charge sixty-five pounds a day! Nearly
two grand a month... money down the
drain... just like the bloody rent...

ABBY

But it's their risk... [anxious] if something
happens...

RICKY

Not one scratch in twenty-five years! I'm
guaranteed £155 a day with the franchise. I'll
be faster than the rest, just like Henry... he's
on over two-hundred quid. 1,200 a week!

ABBY

But that's gross… fourteen hours a day… six
days a week, we hardly see each other as it is!

RICKY

Will be tough as hell at the start… get a year
under my belt, expand the franchise… some of
these boys have five drivers… so who knows?

ABBY

[Doubting] All these stories…

RICKY

If we don't take the leap now… [hesitating,
looking at her] we'll be stuck renting for the
rest of our lives… kicked out whenever it suits
them… I'm sick of moving.

She just looks at him. She can see he is desperate to have a go.

RICKY (CONT'D)

I'll work like a dog.

ABBY

You always have… I just don't know if I
believe in it anymore.

RICKY

Got to have a crack now… it's a young man's
game… time ticks on. But we need a thousand
pound deposit for the van.

ABBY

Ricky, we're already in debt! The only thing
we're not paying off is the car…

He gives her a look. The penny drops, and her face darkens.

                    ABBY (CONT'D)
          Ah no, you can't ask me that... sell the car? [It
          hits her] It's not just about me Ricky...

Ricky just holds her eye.

                    ABBY (CONT'D)
          Miss Sproat... Old Joe... they're in their
          nineties... they'll be devastated... I can't make
          it all the way out there on a bus...

                    RICKY
          Someone with a car can go.

                    ABBY
          Don't understand Ricky... it's their last days...
          they have a right to see the same face...
          they're so... fragile... could finish them off.

                    RICKY
          You're too soft Abby... do the mornings,
          lunches, and be back for the kids and I'll take
          up the slack. Imagine two years from now...
          get a deposit together... in our own home...
          [Passionately] Know what got me? [Pause]
          What you said about decorating... your own
          colours... just the way you want... that's a
          life-changer Abby... It's our turn sweetheart,
          maybe the last chance.

Ricky hugs her. Silence for a few moments. The door flies open
and Seb barges in. He's soaking wet and only has a hoodie on
with his backpack on his shoulder.

RICKY (CONT'D)
It's a bit late son… where were you?

ABBY
Soaking… where's your coat Seb?

SEB
Are you okay Mum?

ABBY
I'm fine son… just trying to make some
plans…

Seb is suspicious. His eyes glance from all the papers on the table
to his mum.

SEB
What's wrong?

ABBY
Your dad is going to set up his own business.

RICKY
Just signed the franchise.

SEB
Wao… taking over McDonald's!

Ricky's face darkens. Seb's phone rings.

SEB (CONT'D)
Joking… what kind of franchise?

ABBY
Delivery franchise… your dad's going to buy
a van.

                              SEB
        Ah… a white van man.

He answers the ringing phone.

                         SEB (CONT'D)
        Harpoon! What's up?

He marches out of the sitting room towards the kitchen. He
opens the drawers and cupboards with far too much energy; the
clatter of spoon and plate roughly thrown down.

Ricky and Abby glance at each other as the teenage chaos
continues.

                         SEB (CONT'D)
        [Unhinging another cupboard] I asked you to
        get more cereal.

                             ABBY
        It's right in front of your eyes sweetheart.

LATER: LIZA JANE'S BEDROOM: Ricky slips in to check
on Liza Jane. As usual she has half-kicked off the cover. Her
cuddly elephant has fallen to the ground. It is worn and full of
holes. Ricky picks it up. He smells it; full of her. He lays it on
her chest. He gently pulls the downie over her and kisses her
forehead.

4. VAN DEALERSHIP, ENTRANCE

Abby drives her car for the last time into the dealership. [Ricky
and Liza Jane are inside.] It disappears among the hundreds of
white vans in the forecourt.

5. TOWARDS AND INTO THE DEPOT, NEWCASTLE – EARLY MORNING

Ricky drives his white van through the industrial estate towards the depot. Liza Jane has drawn a homemade card with a big heart which she has stuck to the dashboard. 'Good luck Dad, love Liza Jane.'

Ricky approaches the depot which has one huge main entrance.

Outside in the forecourt there is a lorry with the company logo PDF that has just delivered a load of parcels. There are a half-dozen white vans outside waiting to enter the depot.

INSIDE: The busiest part of the daily ritual is already underway. There is a sense of order amongst the steady action, with Maloney on site, keeping a careful watch for any glitch.

The depot has six white vans along one side, and another six along the other, forming an L of vehicles up against two walls. About half of them have the same company logo, PDF. On the third side (to the right of the entrance as one enters) there is an enclosed office space for the depot admin. The fourth wall, next to the entrance, is now taken up with large cages full of parcels unloaded from the lorry that has just left.

Four loaders/sorters work at speed, each with a cage, quickly unloading parcels from their cage into the multiple drivers' cages according to the postcodes. Each parcel is quickly scanned by a HHD [a handheld device] known as a gun. Once scanned by the loader/sorter the parcel now has the status of being 'confirmed at location' ie off the lorry and into the depot.

The repetitive bleeps from the guns scanning are heard above the sound of banter. Swarming behind the loader/sorters above, are the drivers, one for each van, each with their own HHD.

One or two of the drivers push their cages across the depot to the back of their vans and scan the parcels again – which means that the parcel is now assigned in the system to a driver with a specific route and postcode, and can be traced.

CHARGING STATION FOR THE HHDs: Maloney instructs Ricky in how to use the HHD.

MALONEY

> This, Ricky, is the heartbeat of the depot...
> Hand Held Device... we call it a gun...
> precious and costs a fortune... if you lose
> it, you pay for it, look after it, it looks after
> you... once you scan the parcel into your
> van that means it's yours, in the system, and
> we can track it every inch of the way to the
> doorstep... it works out the route for you
> too... child's play... but get this through
> your head... 'Precisers', parcels that have to
> be delivered at precise times... you have one
> hour slots... you don't miss them... ever.

Sense of speed and pressure; drivers push their cages across the depot to their vans and load up.

Ricky is back at his van, but he is slower than the rest.

Henry's van is alongside Ricky's. He finishes loading before Ricky and comes over to lend a hand with the parcels.

HENRY

> Doing fine... but got to keep it sharp...
> Remember... first in, last out... get the order
> right, save a nervous breakdown... you've
> got to hit your ETAs... Estimated Times of

Arrival... all on your gun... [There is a smaller
pile of parcels on the ground by the back door,
indicating] Are these your precisers? [Ricky
nods] Good... keep these bastards together,
close at hand... [indicating a separate pile]
you have one hour slots... can't be a second
late... they can be all over the place and cause
havoc... miss these times [indicating Maloney]
and Maloney goes for blood... miss too many
and you get a sanction, three sanctions and
you're out... [indicating, holding the HHD]...
you have to watch out for the gun too...
sometimes the route it gives is shit... and some
of them are just plain dodgy and play up... if
that happens... hours on your day and pure
misery... so get the same one each day... okay?

The driver on the other side needs Ricky to close his back doors
to be on his way.

DRIVER
Come on man... enough of the yap... let's get
a move on...

HENRY
[Joking] You were a donkey for your first
month, so zip it! [To Ricky, quietly] Ignore
him... couldn't kick shite along a gutter...
he's a subcontracted driver to big Sam...
[indicating with nod of the head] it's Sam's
van... Sam gets 170 guaranteed for the
route...

RICKY
How much does he get for driving?

                    HENRY
Just seventy.

                    RICKY
Fucking hell…

                    HENRY
Nail this… and you get a better route…
fucking cut-throat. One last thing… most
important of all…

Henry grabs an empty plastic bottle and throws it to him.

                HENRY (CONT'D)
You'll need this… [Ricky is confused] for a
piss…

                    RICKY
Winding me up…

                    HENRY
You'll see…

                    RICKY
Fuck off.

Maloney [while having his barcode scanned by a couple drivers
so they can leave] is keeping up the pressure and shouts out above
the noise to everyone.

                   MALONEY
Come on! Hit the road!

                      31

6. ROADS IN THE CITY AND COUNTRY

Ricky is making deliveries. His journey gives an overview of Newcastle and the surrounding area.

A. BRIDGE OVER THE TYNE
Ricky is driving, alert, seen through the windscreen as he drives across the bridge. One behind the other, the bridges reveal the scale of the city.

B. A TERRACED STREET
Inside the van, the cabin has been transformed by drawings and love hearts, drawn by Lisa Jane. There is also a photograph of the family together. Ricky checks the numbers of the houses as he drives. The van pulls up. No space, so he double parks, blocking the road. He runs to the back of his vehicle, gun in hand, opens the back door and grabs a parcel. Locks it again. He runs up a flight of stairs, rings the bell and scans the parcel. A car horn blares. Ricky gestures − 'couple of minutes'. A woman with a toddler opens the door, signs for the parcel.

C. CITY CENTRE
Ricky drives down Victorian streets on bending slopes, down under the Tyne Bridge near the Quayside. There is no parking so he pulls up on the pavement. He is looking for an office address but some numbers are missing. He presses an intercom − it's the wrong one, no help offered. He stands back, surveying business names on the plaques. Confusion.

D. DUAL CARRIAGEWAY
Heavy traffic. Ricky at the wheel again.

E. AN OLD INDUSTRIAL AREA
The van picks its way through the wasteland of an old industrial estate, with the outlines where factories and offices once stood. A few working buildings remain. Ricky peers through the windscreen, looking for an address.

F. CITY CENTRE

Near Grey's Monument. Ricky is parked illegally. Parcels in hand, he is pleading with a traffic warden to give him a few minutes.

G. A BLOCK OF MAISONETTES

Ricky runs up the steps, carrying a heavy parcel. A door opens. A bare-chested man holding a drip above his head (it goes straight into his body) appears.

> CUSTOMER
> That's my grub... thanks very much.

> RICKY
> A pleasure mate. Glad to help. It's heavy... can
> I put it somewhere for you?

H. MODERN EX-COUNCIL HOUSE

Ricky walks down the garden path, rings the bell and scans the parcel. The door opens and an intimidating figure fills the entrance, wearing a Newcastle United top. In a split second he notices a small Manchester United motif on Ricky's shirt.

> CUSTOMER
> Typical [pointing] bloody United fan! Never
> from Manchester...

> RICKY
> Not me mate, 100 per cent Manc!

As he signs the customer revels in taking the piss, rubbing it in.

> CUSTOMER
> Ah must have been torture... Agüero's goal...
> extra time... shirt off... a blue shirt... waving

to the fans… [holding his eye] City fans…
United pipped to the title, last kick of the
ball… [a huge sarcastic grin] a tragedy…

RICKY

[Nodding] I was suicidal… only saved by
YouTube… every time I thought of that goal
[he hands over the parcel] I had to put on
Kevin Keegan's rant, with the popping eyes…
'I'd love it if I beat them… I'd love it!' And
what happened? We did you! King Eric, one
nil. Won the league!

As Ricky heads off chuckling the customer gives him the fingers.

CUSTOMER

Fuck off!!

RICKY

Ooh ah Cantona!!!

7. ROSIE'S HOUSE

Abby walks quickly along a road until she comes to Rosie's
house. She moves to a wall. Behind flowers she finds a key box
which has a code. She dials that and extracts a key.

Before entering, she has a ritual. She takes out a stick of Vicks,
and rubs it just under her nose on the top lip and enters the house.

ABBY

Rosie… it's me, Abby. How are you?

She peeks into the sitting room, then kitchen, but nobody is
there.

ABBY (CONT'D)
Rosie... are you having a wee rest?

She checks the bedroom. Nobody there. Then the bathroom.

ABBY (CONT'D)
Where are you Rosie... it's me... Abby.

She goes back to the bedroom, checks behind the curtains, and then gently opens the doors to a sizeable wardrobe. She can see a pair of frightened eyes look up at her.

ABBY (CONT'D)
Rosie... what's wrong sweetheart? Is it hide and seek?

Abby leans in to help her, taking her hand.

ABBY (CONT'D)
Ah darling... you're frozen... what's wrong?

ROSIE
Is he gone yet?

ABBY
Who Rosie?

ROSIE
There's a strange man in my house... he keeps coming...

ABBY
Ah sweetheart...

LATER: KITCHEN TABLE: Abby is multitasking. She is trying to spoon-feed Rosie an omelette she has just cooked. Between bites Abby is counting out Rosie's tablets, and then she types in two codes into Rosie's landline phone. The first is her own carer's number, and then that of the patient. She gives Rosie another bite and then starts to fill in the diary with notes.

                    ABBY (CONT'D)
          That's not a stranger Rosie... that's your new
          carer... he comes to tuck you in, check your
          medicine... Okay? So don't be scared.

Rosie pushes away the omelette.

                    ROSIE
          Let's chat!

                    ABBY
          Okay Rosie... but let's chat and [fishing back
          the plate] finish your lunch...

                    ROSIE
          There's a strange man in my house...

                    ABBY
          That's your new carer Rosie.

                    ROSIE
          Can I comb your hair?

                    ABBY
          If you finish your omelette...

She shoves the plate of food crashing to the floor.

8. ROBERT'S FLAT, LATER

Abby is again multitasking. In the kitchen she empties some scrambled egg onto a plate, pours a cup of tea, grabs some toast that has just popped up, takes a glass of water and carries it all through on a tray towards the living room. As she passes the toilet in the hall she calls out.

> ABBY
> That's it all ready Robert, just the way you like it.

A frail voice calls to her.

> ROBERT
> Thank you Abby.

In the living room Abby counts out two sets of tablets, writes up the diary quickly, and then takes out a sanitary pad for an adult from her bag and spreads it out, ready for use.

Back to her ritual; she smears some Vicks over her top lip. She moves to the hallway. The toilet door is slightly ajar. We can see an old man's bare legs as he sits on the toilet.

> ABBY
> How are you doing Robert... nearly there?

> ROBERT
> It's so sore Abby... so sore.

> ABBY
> [Checking her watch] Take your time... give me a shout and I can wipe you down and put on a fresh pad...

ROBERT

Thank you Abby... you never rush me like
the others... I always pray it's you... you're a
gem...

ABBY

Thank you Robert.

ROBERT

[Almost to himself] I never thought this
would happen to me...

9. A BUS, TRAVELLING THROUGH SUBURBS

Abby is on the phone to Liza Jane.

ABBY

It's in the big Tupperware on the bottom
shelf, heat it up. I'll try and get back as soon as
I can... fifteen minutes on the computer after
homework, no more! Leave out your project
and I'll check it when I get back... bed,
quarter to nine sharp! No... your dad won't
be back till very late... Love you sweetheart...

Abby dials another number but it goes onto answer machine
mode.

ABBY (CONT'D)

[Frustrated] Seb... did you get my message?
That's another text in from the school...
where have you been? Can't believe it... good
job your dad's not getting these... where the
hell are you?... Phone me NOW!

She checks her watch.

10. HOME – LATE AFTERNOON

Liza Jane, in school uniform, with her bag dangling from her shoulder, walks back home from school. She approaches the front door with keys in her hand.

INSIDE THE FRONT DOOR, BY THE SHELF: Sound of the door opening. Liza Jane throws her keys (with a distinctive dolphin key ring) on the shelf, which is empty.

She climbs the stairs and moves through to the kitchen after dumping her bag down with a thump. She pours herself some cereal, adds the milk, and she can hear the Rice Krispies pop in the stillness of the empty house. Her mobile indicates there is a message from Snapchat and her face brightens. She swipes to reveal the image; it is her best friend in her home too, by herself, eating Rice Krispies. (They are on a Snapchat 'streak' between them, sending each other an image each day continuously to build up a run. After the image is revealed on the screen, it disappears, literally a snap.) Liza Jane takes a quick snap of herself eating Rice Krispies too, an almost identical copy of that sent by her friend, and sends it to her in return. All done in an instant, another daily ritual of contact. She goes on munching on her cereal in the silence.

THREE HOURS LATER: Seb and Liza Jane by themselves, eat their evening meals in front of the computer. They are transfixed by a video from Seb's mobile, which is connected to the computer screen (some of which makes Liza Jane giggle). The images are taken on his smartphone by Seb's friend, Roz, and feature Seb giving a demo on how to paint a simple graffiti bird-like image in profile (quite elegant) to his other mate Harpoon, while a third mate, Dodge, keeps an eye out for them.

It is all a bit chaotic; Roz and Harpoon try not to laugh at Seb's growing frustration with them all.

They are in front of a wall by a narrow path in the centre of Newcastle. Images of Seb shaking his spray paint can ready for use, intermixed with Roz turning the camera on herself, clowning around and perhaps making daft faces into the camera, and generally testing his patience.

                    SEB
        Roz! Will you stop pissing around! Dodge…
        [camera turns on another lad] go down there
        a bit and keep a look out for us… [he does]…
        I've really thought about this image… it's
        special and marks us out. Got to be simple…
        to do it quick or the cops catch you… [to
        Harpoon] even you could master this… four
        quick swishes… now I'm going to do it here
        [picking a space on the wall] and you're going
        to do it there… [to Roz] get in close… I want
        you to do it exactly like this.

He does the four sprays at speed like a professional as he counts out the swipes.

                    SEB (CONT'D)
        One! [Outer dome of the head] Two! [Little
        eye] Three! [Little line under the eye] Four!
        [Tiny beak] What do you think?

It does look impressive.

                    ROZ
        Classy… really classy. Could be a logo.

                    SEB
        Correct. [To Harpoon] Right you… do the
        same right there…

Harpoon takes a deep breath. He has two cans, one in each hand.

                    DODGE
          All clear...

                    HARPOON
          This will blow your mind... I should be on
          the telly...

                    SEB
          Shut up and just do it.

With both cans, at the same time, demonstrating outstanding control, he draws with both hands, two copies of the bird. Big grin on his face as he finishes.

Seb is stunned and can't believe it. Two perfect birds.

                    SEB (CONT'D)
          Can't believe it man. [Admiring, back to
          camera] It's perfect... just the way I want it...

He turns as he hears more spraying. He can't believe his eyes as Harpoon goes back to the image again and quickly draws in a pair of red legs and feet, totally screwing it up.

                    SEB (CONT'D)
          Oh no! Shit!

                    HARPOON
          That's going to go viral man...

Next he adds on a few tufts of hair on both birds.

SEB

I'll tell you what's going to go viral... me
kicking your stupid arse round Newcastle!

Seb chases after him as he flees while Liza Jane laughs.

LATER: Liza Jane is in bed. She hears the front door slam.
She goes to the window, peers between the curtains. She sees
Seb greet his three mates from the video (Harpoon, Dodge,
and Roz), all three with bulging small rucksacks on, before
disappearing into the night.

The sound of the TV. Liza Jane's bedroom door opens and she
goes to the living room. Abby and Ricky are fast asleep on the
sofa. Abby's head leans on Ricky's shoulder. Dirty plates on trays,
one meal only half-eaten, sit before them on a little table. Beside
that are a pile of receipts, diesel etc, rows of figures in Ricky's
hand, and a calculator.

Liza Jane stares at them for a moment, and then switches the
telly off. The sudden silence wakes up Ricky. He catches sight
of Liza Jane staring at him. He beckons her over. She jumps into
his lap and he pulls her in tight and kisses the top of her head.

RICKY

Scallywag Tadpole.

LIZA JANE

You were snoring.

RICKY

It was your mum.

ABBY

It was your dad.

FADE

11. INSIDE DEPOT – MORNING

The drivers are loading up their vans. Maloney is giving a driver, Freddy (who is less scared than most and defends himself) a right bollocking. The edginess builds, and all the drivers are aware. Freddy has a bottle of water in his hand.

FREDDY

I called you this morning, three times, no
answer! Someone whacked my mirror...
knocked it off.

MALONEY

Why didn't you bloody well fix it last night?

FREDDY

It happened early, first thing... parked outside
the house... is that my fault?

MALONEY

Well get a replacement driver!

FREDDY

Just give me two hours, that's all I'm asking...

MALONEY

What good is that to me? Waiting two
fucking hours... you know the rule... be here
first thing, or get a replacement!

FREDDY

I've worked fourteen days in a row! Fourteen!
I'm only asking for two hours... you never
give an inch...

MALONEY

Because you're always bloody moaning, always
phoning, some fecking excuse... and you
missed three precisers last week.

FREDDY

You gave me far too many... and you fucking
know it!

All goes quiet in the depot, their attention taken up by the row.

MALONEY

I can sort that! I'll give your route to someone
who doesn't whinge all day, hits their
numbers...

FREDDY

Trying to squeeze me out... just like Stevie.
Same old story!

MALONEY

Couldn't sell a black cat to a fucking witch!

Maloney asks a driver near Ricky.

MALONEY (CONT'D)

Davie, are you up for a busier run? Up for a
challenge without whining?

DRIVER

Stick where I am... Sally's not so well...

Maloney spots Ricky who is loading up beside Henry.

MALONEY

Ricky, you've been racing around without a
fuss... want a better route?

Ricky hesitates, confused.

MALONEY (CONT'D)
Not hungry enough? He's fucking lost the
route no matter what... so do you want it?

RICKY
I don't know...

MALONEY
Make up your mind.

A moment. Henry nods at Ricky and mouths 'Take it!'

RICKY
[Quietly] Okay...

MALONEY
[Holding his eye and smiling] That's my
boy! Right you two swap routes... swap
the details... [to Freddy] and if you don't
like it you can fucking walk, right now! [To
everyone] Right, entertainment over...

Ricky approaches Freddy with the gun.

RICKY
Sorry mate... didn't mean to take your
route...

FREDDY
Fuck off.

Maloney is still watching them both from the office door.

MALONEY
Swap routes I said! Move it!

Ricky is stunned when Freddy, with all his fury, hurls the bottle of water towards Maloney. It just misses him and smashes by the door. Freddy sprints towards Maloney, who just gets inside his office and slams the door shut a second before Freddy crashes up against it. He totally loses it. Berserk, as Maloney desperately tries to keep the door shut with his weight. A half-dozen drivers grab Freddy, trying to calm him down.

VOICES
Cool it Freddy… Easy man… Calm down
man… he's not worth it.

They overwhelm him as a startled Maloney peeks through a crack. Ricky is down, feeling guilty, as he sees Freddy struggling among the drivers.

FREDDY
Let me take the bastard… fucking sick of all
the shit!

12. GROUND FLOOR FLAT IN A SMALL MODERN
BLOCK – MORNING

Abby tries to calm down an irate younger man, Ben, who is still in his bed, but who is incapable of getting up himself. He is agitated, and hard to handle.

BEN
Please… please, just leave be… if you get me up
now… I'll just be sitting there all day for hours
and hours… for what?! For fuck all! Staring at
the walls! Can you not just leave me in peace!!

ABBY

I'm sorry Ben, but please don't swear at me.

BEN

Come back later!

ABBY

Ben… I have six other people to care for, to
wake up, get them up and give breakfast to…
I can't be in two places at one time… I'm
really sorry to get you up so early… I've got
your breakfast all ready, piping hot… just the
way you like it.

BEN

I'm not moving… that's it.

Abby sighs and checks her watch.

BEN (CONT'D)

I just want to blank it all out…

ABBY

Okay, okay… [looking at her timetable]
Ben… it's okay, don't get yourself upset… let's
see… let's see… what if I come back in two
hours?

BEN

Why didn't you say that in the first fucking
place?

Abby takes a deep breath.

ABBY

I have a break then... so that's my time...
I'll come back then... okay? All I ask is that
you don't swear at me... and treat me with
respect... okay? I won't stand for swearing.

BEN

Give me peace...

Another deep breath and Abby pulls the blanket up over him.
She moves into the hall and pulls out her phone and dials.

13. HOME – MORNING

SEB'S BEDROOM: A curtain sweeps open, letting in the
light. A typical teenager's room, and the fug of dirty clothes
all over. Some spray paint cans are on the floor by a rucksack.
Seb is stuck to the bed as only a teenager can be. Liza Jane
hovers above him.

LIZA JANE

Mum's been phoning... Come on Seb...
you're late again... move it! [He just turns
over.] Dad'll go crazy if he finds out...

14. STREET OF OLD TERRACED HOUSES: A GABLE END

Seb, Harpoon, Dodge and Roz approach a blank gable end
of a wall. It is a dilapidated corner by a busy street, with lots
of traffic sailing by.

Scaffolding is in front of the gable end and the first phase of
putting up an advert is underway; a blank boarding now awaits
the advert. They look up at it, excited by the possibilities.

ROZ

I told you it was a great spot…

SEB

They'll soon have the advert up… selling
more shit. Let's go for it.

HARPOON

We'll never get any time before they're on
us… not worth it, man…

Seb pulls out four yellow hi–vis vests from his rucksack. [The
capital letters OBK have been drawn on them with a thick
black marker.]

SEB

Put these on…

DODGE

Fuck! They'll see us from miles away…

ROZ

That's why they're called 'hi-vis'… [at his
growing confusion] that's the point.

Before they know it, Seb has his vest on and is halfway up the
scaffolding followed by Roz. They pull themselves onto the
planks. With some hesitation, the other two follow. Harpoon
shoots up like a squirrel but Dodge keeps sliding down and
making a balls of it. Seb has to lend a hand, and tries to pull
him up by the arm as he scrambles over the ledge.

SEB

Not cut out for harvesting coconuts are you?

DODGE

Nearly pulled my arm off. [Rubbing his arm
and shoulder] Feels like six inches longer...

HARPOON

Should have grabbed him by his parsnip...

They get cans of spray paint from their bags. Seb gives his a
shake and starts to mark out the drawings: he has clearly done
this before. Then a van from the local parks dept screeches to
a halt and an irate official marches towards them.

HARPOON (CONT'D)

[To Seb, irate] Fucking told you smart arse...
and not even started yet...

OFFICIAL

What a brass neck! Right in the middle of a
school day... Get down!

SEB

It is school sir, an outreach project with the
Open University and the police... they put up
the scaffolding... [pointing to the letters OBK
on the hi-vis jackets] 'O. B. K.'

OFFICIAL

O. B. What?

SEB

'Out Back Krew'... for disadvantaged youth
from an under-privileged background...

ROZ

With learning difficulties.

OFFICIAL

Is that a female up there?

HARPOON

That's gender discrimination... you should
know better.

OFFICIAL

[Peering at the letters] Where's your
supervisor?

SEB

She's not a supervisor... what do you call her
Roz?

ROZ

A 'curator'.

SEB

The curator! She's gone to meet the sergeant
up at the station... I've got her mobile
somewhere if you want to give her a call...

He looks at them suspiciously.

OFFICIAL

[Hesitating] I'll be back...

HARPOON

Do you think you could bring some red paint
if you get a chance mate? But don't go out of
your way...

The official quietly fumes, and heads to his van.

SEB

  We have about thirty minutes… let's move it.

He is shaking the can again as he contemplates the blank canvas, the entire gable end.

HARPOON

  Nice one… hi-vis… [to Seb] you actually
  planned that…

SEB

  It's how you look at things… some pricks can't
  see what's right in front of their eyes…

Seb makes the first big confident sweeping curl on the wall with his white spray can. With another few flourishes that take just seconds we see the outline of an exaggerated mouth in profile; it is memorable and sticks in the mind. Clear he has talent. Roz is beside Seb and she too makes her start with a spray can.

ROZ

  Can I do the OBK? My last one.

SEB

  What are you talking about?

ROZ

  I'm leaving… got my ticket to Blackpool.

SEB

  We need you here Roz, with us… what's up?

ROZ

  Serious hassle man… can't stand it.

                          SEB
        What happened?

She ignores him and starts to spray the letters OBK. Seb stops
to watch for a second.

                          ROZ
        Something to remember me by...

15. STREETS

Ricky is stuck in traffic, in city motorways.

LATER: Ricky pleads with a taciturn neighbour, eating a slice
of toast, to take a parcel for his next-door neighbour.

                         RICKY
        Would you mind taking this parcel for your
        neighbour?

                       NEIGHBOUR
        [Shaking his head] Bastard keeps taking my
        parking spot...

Ricky looks up and down the abandoned street fifty metres
each way.

                         RICKY
        Sorry to hear that mate... could you do me
        the favour... I don't get paid till I deliver...

                       NEIGHBOUR
        He's a wanker.

But he takes it reluctantly.

RICKY

Many thanks... just sign here... [he does]
can't quite read that, can I have your name
please?

NEIGHBOUR

[Shaking his head] Big data...

RICKY

Big what?

NEIGHBOUR

Big data... these bastards hoover up our
personal information... from that [indicating
HHD] black box to cyberspace... next
thing... [he squeezes the sizeable package in
his arm which is very squidgy] I'll be getting
brochures on blow up dolls... because that's
what I think this is... he's a fucking pervert!
Can tell by the way he parks.

He steps inside and slams the door shut in Ricky's face.

RICKY

Holy fuck.

Fortunately, his name is on the door in a big bright letters. Ricky
peers at it, and writes it in his gun.

17. MOLLIE'S HOME

The ground floor of a modest home. Mollie, in her wheelchair,
has great presence. Frail in body, but sharp in mind. Mollie
prepares the tea. Abby looks at two memorable black and white
photos in pride of place on a shelf. They are from the miners'
strike in 1984. One is a photo of a packed room in the miners'

club in Easington village with a woman in the middle of the
photo serving lunch from a huge pot. [Two little boys are staring
at the food being served.] The other photo is of a single woman,
in her early thirties, holding her head in her hands, in shock,
talking to a man in a suit with his back to the camera.

ABBY
Love these photos Mollie… so alive…

MOLLIE
Bring them over… [peering into the first]
that was our free caf during the miners' strike
in '84… can tell it was the summer as we
borrowed the pots from the school…

ABBY
It's packed… [smiling] look at the lads staring
at the grub!

MOLLIE
Ah… wee Blackett boy… we fed over five
hundred every day…

ABBY
Five hundred?!

MOLLIE
[Indicating woman in the middle dishing out
the food] That's Marilyn Johnstone… she
worked at the chemist's and gave up her lunch
hour every day as a volunteer… me too… I
came down from the Council office… but I
brought my own packed lunch as my husband
wasn't a miner…

ABBY

[Pointing to the other] That poor woman
looks shocked...

MOLLIE

That poor woman was me! [Pointing to a man
in a suit with his back to photo] That was
Benny... NUM official... nearly gave me a
bloody heart attack... that was the second he
told me there were two busses of pickets just
arrived... and could we feed them too.

ABBY

On top of the five hundred?! [Mollie nods]
Bloody hell.

MOLLIE

We only had one cooker and two boilers!
You should have heard the language in the
kitchen... including my mam... but somehow
we did it...

ABBY

Unbelievable...

MOLLIE

We set up fourteen free cafs all round East
Durham... fourteen!

ABBY

Must bring back memories Mollie...

Mollie is quiet for a moment, remembering those days, the
intimacy of friendship and solidarity; and betrayal.

MOLLIE

We were all so close... pulled us together...
never the same again... fills me with pride still
to this day... and breaks my heart...

It takes her a moment to recover.

MOLLIE (CONT'D)

Now where's your photos... you promised
me...

ABBY

Ah Mollie... I can't show you after these...
mine are just little family snaps...

MOLLIE

We're all one big family! And never you forget
it! Come on... you promised me... I won't
take no...

Abby relents and reaches into her bag and lays the photos (some
loose, and a few in frames) on the table as Mollie pours the tea.

ABBY

So busy... I just grabbed a few off the wall
too.

Abby first puts down a photo of herself, Ricky and a five-year-
old Seb, just inside the gate of a modest terraced house. They
all look so happy; Seb holds Abby's arm, and Ricky, beaming
has one arm round Abby's shoulder, with the other flat on her
tummy.

MOLLIE

You look gorgeous! Blooming.

ABBY

I was pregnant with Liza Jane… Six months…

MOLLIE

And look how happy Ricky is… where did
you meet?

Abby takes out another photo: the two of them when young,
messing around, outside a distinctive building, the Empire in
Morecambe.

ABBY

The mad days… used to be buses from
Newcastle to Morecambe for weekend raves…
that's outside the Empire… [They both stare
at the photo] Ricky used to come up from
Manchester in his battered old van…

MOLLIE

[Peering at the photo] A handsome lad…

ABBY

I would never call him that… but he was so
attractive… made me feel special… could say
anything to him…

MOLLIE

That's what I call 'soul mates'.

A hint of sadness in Abby's eye.

ABBY

And he had so much energy… never
stopped… at least that hasn't changed…

Another photo of Ricky and Seb playing together when he was just ten.

                    ABBY (CONT'D)
         And he was great with Seb.

                      MOLLIE
         You can see that.

There are others with Ricky and Seb, having fun, perhaps camping. Three of these photos are from the stairs in the flat. Back again to the photo outside the house.

                  MOLLIE (CONT'D)
         Is that your house?

Abby sighs.

                       ABBY
         We thought it was... price agreed... that
         was taken one week before Northern Rock
         collapsed... remember, ten years ago... Ricky
         was in the building trade... tons of work...
         all dried up in a month... one crappy job
         after another ever since. The mortgage fell
         through so we lost the house... been renting
         ever since... moved so many times... sick of it
         [flicking over to another] that's Liza Jane now,
         cheeky scamp...

                      MOLLIE
         Bright as a button.

                       ABBY
         [Another] And Seb... changing in front of my
         eyes... when I see him.

Mollie senses her guilt.

                    MOLLIE
        Is your family around to lend a hand?

                    ABBY
        [Sigh] Long story that... my mam died
        three years back... and Ricky's are down in
        Manchester.

Abby catches herself and then checks her watch.

                    ABBY (CONT'D)
        Better run your bath... [gathering up the
        photos, chuckling] I could get disciplined for
        this... don't get close to 'the clients' they told
        us... I just can't use that word.

Mollie smiles in appreciation.

                    MOLLIE
        What time's your next appointment?

Abby has her timetable out before her, marked Employee Rota.
Her finger runs down the column.

                    ABBY
        Got the next two hours free... that's why we
        can chat...

                    MOLLIE
        Hope they pay you.

                    ABBY
        Zero-hour contract... only pay you for the
        visits...

MOLLIE

Travelling time?

ABBY

Not a chance... pay our own bus fares...

Mollie peers over the timetable.

MOLLIE

It's all stretched out... from 7.30am... till 9
tonight... [incredulous] can't be right... what
happened to the eight–hour day?

ABBY

I'll cut back when we clear some debts.

MOLLIE

It's worse than we had... I keep saying to the
youngsters... you've got to get together...

ABBY

Truth is, us carers, we hardly see each other...

We sense the steel in Mollie.

MOLLIE

By yourself, they pick you off... you have to
join a union... and if the union isn't good
enough... you make them good enough!

ABBY

They dump the troublemakers... we're in
debt... I just can't risk it for the family...

MOLLIE

I understand darling… I'm not judging you…
but there'll come a time when you've had
enough… mark my words… that's when you
know you have the power… when you come
together.

18A. BUS STATION, NEWCASTLE – DAY

Long walkway parallel to the busses through the station which
is packed with people. In and among the throng, Seb and Roz
walk through the station. Between them, holding a strap each,
they carry a sizeable bag.

SEB

Have you got enough water?

ROZ

I'm fine…

SEB

I don't even know where Blackpool is…

ROZ

As long as the driver knows…

They move to the appropriate waiting area which is separated
out for each destination by sets of metal seats. They take a seat
to wait for the bus. Seb looks jumpy.

SEB

Who are you going to stay with?

ROZ

A friend of a friend… she works in a guest
house… cleaning… I can crash with her till

I find a job... all sorts down there... the gift
shops, the Pleasure Beach, the fair... even
Madame Tussauds and it has one of the biggest
roller coasters ever, Pepsi Max they call it...
it's all fun down there... not like here...

                    SEB
What happened Roz?

She hesitates and fidgets with her cigarette lighter.

                    ROZ
Those girls jumped me again... pulled out
clumps of hair and really hurt me... they'll
never leave me alone... bullies are for life
unless you move...

                    SEB
But why are they doing it?

                    ROZ
I'm just a bit different... easy to pick on.
It's gone on since school. And my mum's
boyfriend is a bully too... I've had enough...
inside the house, outside the house...

The bus driver opens the bus door so passengers can get on.

                    SEB
We'll never find the great spots without you...

She shrugs and smiles.

                    SEB (CONT'D)
Have you got a sandwich or something?

ROZ

I'm not hungry.

SEB

Send a text when you arrive…

She just nods. She climbs on the bus with her bag which seems to dwarf her. She takes a seat by the window and shyly waves at Seb.

Seb looks at her for a moment, nods at her, and walks off briskly.

18B. HOME

IN THE LIVING ROOM: Ricky is in the process of extracting cans of paint from Seb's rucksack. There are about a dozen. The last couple are crashed down with force.

RICKY

How did you pay for all these?

SEB

We all chipped in…

ABBY

Please Seb… just tell us…

There is something so jaded about his mum's face that he changes tack.

SEB

He'll go fucking bonkers…

ABBY

Please Seb… [to Ricky too] both of you…
you know swearing upsets me… my father
swore all the time…

Silence for a moment.

                    SEB
          I sold my new jacket.

Abby's face drops too.

                    ABBY
          Supposed to last you the winter son.

                    RICKY
          The Gore-Tex? Know how much that cost
          us!? For fuck's sake!!

Seb smirks (what did I tell you) which makes Ricky's blood boil.

                    RICKY (CONT'D)
          Jesus Christ… are you up on roofs… on train
          tracks?! An all that shite over the walls?

                    ABBY
          Can we just speak?

                    SEB
          There is a lot of shite on the walls…
          everywhere. It's called advertising…

                    RICKY
          What the fuck are you on about?

                    ABBY
          Please…

The row escalates…

UPSTAIRS: Liza Jane lies in her bed. Her fingers nervously twist one of the ears of her cuddly elephant. She can hear the sound of distant shouts, and the tension upsets her.

IN THE KITCHEN:

> RICKY
> Were you at school today?

Seb just stares at the ground.

> RICKY (CONT'D)
> How many days have you missed in the last month?

More determined silence which drives Ricky to exasperation.

> RICKY (CONT'D)
> We'll be dragged up before an Attendance Panel... that's what the last letter said... me and your mum will face a fine! Is that what you want?

Still silence.

> RICKY (CONT'D)
> Just don't get it Seb... you've got brains to burn... you were always in the top five... always quick... Liza Jane's the same... Jesus Christ... get yourself some qualifications, some choices...

> ABBY
> You could go to uni.

SEB

Yeah, like Harpoon's brother? Fifty-seven
grand in debt! Now in a call centre... so
miserable he gets smashed every weekend to
block it out!

RICKY

Doesn't have to be that... some great jobs
out there if you get stuck in... if you don't...
you'll...

SEB

End up like you.

It stings, and hurts Abby too to see Ricky humiliated.

RICKY

[Very quiet now] That's right Seb... that's
what will happen... one dead-end job after
another, bursting your ass for others, keeping
your mouth shut... doing a fourteen-hour
day... end up a skivvy.

SEB

You don't end up a skivvy Dad... it's a choice.
You choose to be a skivvy.

ABBY

Seb!

Ricky, exhausted, looks at him for a moment. He takes a deep
breath.

RICKY

I'm trying my best Seb... I want it better for
you... but maybe you have to learn the hard
way...

Ricky, done in, heads for bed.

Abby feels it to the pit of her stomach. Silence for a long moment between them.

> ABBY
> You never had a cruel streak in your body
> Seb… where did that come from? Eh?

Seb stares at his hands for a long moment.

> ABBY (CONT'D)
> What's wrong son?

He jumps up suddenly, leaves, and slams the front door behind him.

FADE

19. STREETS

SATURDAY: Liza Jane is helping Ricky as he delivers. She plainly enjoys time with her dad.

A. A WARREN OF CONCRETE FLATS: The van speeds into a parking space. Liza Jane clutching the HHD, and Ricky holding a parcel, run along a pathway to a set of concrete stairs.

> LIZA JANE
> [Glancing at the HHD] Ninety seconds Dad!

Ricky's eyes scan the confusing numbers on a wall.

> RICKY
> This way!

LIZA JANE

Sixty seconds!

They rush up along a walkway, up another set of stairs, and both
panting arrive at a door. Ricky rings the doorbell.

LIZA JANE (CONT'D)

Fifteen seconds…

RICKY

Scan scan scan!

She does, machine up against the barcode, and that familiar
bleep.

LIZA JANE

Made it!!!

Grinning, he holds out his hand and she smacks it.

The door opens. A friendly face of a woman.

WOMAN

Ah, giving your dad a hand sweetheart?

Back to the van, Ricky drives out of the car park, Liza Jane
jingles the tips she has been given.

LIZA JANE

That's the third tip!

RICKY

Gold digger…

LIZA JANE
[Checking the HHD] Come on… another preciser… only eight minutes and two miles away!

B. A MAIN ROAD: With Liza Jane by his side, Ricky drives steadily. She has the HHD in her hand, absorbed by it.

LIZA JANE (CONT'D)
It can text… phone… photograph… scan… sign, contact the customer… anything else?

RICKY
Bloody well bleep! I hear it in my dreams… bleeps if I am out of the cab for more than two minutes…

LIZA JANE
So they know where you are?

RICKY
To the exact metre… and they can track each parcel… to the back door, to the garden shed…

LIZA JANE
Boing! Bouncing off a satellite… right here, into this wee black box… amazing isn't it? Spy in the cab… [She mocks speaking into it] Hello… Liza Jane here… I like bananas!

Ricky chuckles

RICKY
Working out the exact route… the traffic…

the weather... estimated time of arrival... and
cuts out if you arrive early! In case there is a
preciser.

LIZA JANE

But why do they need it to the exact time?

RICKY

What these big companies do now... order
it online before midnight... guarantee it the
next day... if they pay a bit extra... within the
hour...

LIZA JANE

But it means you have to go zig-zagging all
over the place, out of order... do they know
how late you finish?

Ricky glances at her.

RICKY

You're full of questions darling...

LIZA JANE

But who puts it all in here?

RICKY

What do you mean?

LIZA JANE

Somebody must think about it... put all the
information inside... somebody must have
done that... [physically tapping it] I mean
really put it in...

RICKY

Must be a robot, or an app, or a programme…

LIZA JANE

But somebody must feed the robot in the first
place…

RICKY

Some specky geek I suppose…

LIZA JANE

Who never goes to the toilet. [Ricky looks at
her] Well… measure everything else… why
not time for the toilet?

Ricky chuckles and shakes his head.

RICKY

Didn't get those brains from me.

C. OUTSIDE A VICTORIAN HOUSE: Ricky and Liza Jane
have already rung the bell and there is no answer. It is a grand
house and a lovely entrance, a contrast from the others earlier
in the day. Ricky checks the gun.

RICKY (CONT'D)

Says to leave it in the shed round the back…
[handing her a card from his back pocket] fill
out the card for me…

Abby takes the distinctive card and places it up against the door
entrance to write down the details as Ricky disappears down
the side of the house. The card has bold clear letters on the top
of the card: 'SORRY WE MISSED YOU'.

Liza Jane fills out the blank spaces in her childish writing, and then examines the card carefully. In the distance she hears sudden barking, her dad cursing, and a gate crashing. Ricky reappears, red-faced with the fright.

> RICKY (CONT'D)
> Bloody great wolf round there... teeth that size!

They both start laughing.

Liza Jane has second thoughts before popping the card through the letter box.

> LIZA JANE
> [Reading the top line again] Sorry we missed you... [as if adding to info] 'and you owe my dad a fresh pair of Y-fronts!'

Ricky laughs. She pops it through the letter box.

20. BUS SHELTER

Abby and an older woman are waiting for the bus. Abby is in the middle of a heated conversation on the phone and the woman waiting with her can't help but overhear.

Real fire in Abby's belly, and she is spitting mad.

> SUPERVISOR'S VOICE
> An hour, a full hour late! The family are going crazy... all sorts of threats...

> ABBY
> I'll tell you why I'm late... because you never bloody well listen...

SUPERVISOR'S VOICE
Don't you dare talk to me like this!

ABBY
She was half-naked... covered in faeces...
smeared all over the walls... it was in her
clothes, her bed, the bathroom, inside the
front door... it was in her hair, under her
fingernails... she was screaming and crying
for over half an hour... she was slapping me
as I tried to clean the poor soul and for your
information I got covered in it too... she is
terrified of her own daughter who never turns
the heating on... and she was freezing!

SUPERVISOR'S VOICE
Well we know she is a difficult client...

ABBY
I'm not finished yet! This is the third time I've
told you... she is confused, vulnerable and in
danger...

SUPERVISOR'S VOICE
We'll phone the daughter...

ABBY
Do you ever listen?! The daughter doesn't
give a damn!... All she cares about is selling
the house... now if you don't call the
authorities... this is the last warning... I'm
going to go up myself... do I make myself
clear?

SUPERVISOR'S VOICE
Right Abby... calm down...

ABBY

I will not have her on my conscience... last
warning!

SUPERVISOR'S VOICE

Okay Abby...

ABBY

No... not okay Abby... know how long it
took me to clean up? Ninety minutes, flat out,
for a half hour call... Are you going to pay me
the extra hour?

SUPERVISOR'S VOICE

Abby, you know I can't do that...

ABBY

Should I leave the poor soul in her own
excrement all day? [Pause. The woman in the
bus is aghast too] That was a question.

SUPERVISOR'S VOICE

Abby... I didn't know.

ABBY

I'm sick to the back teeth with you all.

SUPERVISOR'S VOICE

Okay Abby... I'm sorry about this... [pause]...
I've had two call-offs... can you do Ms Sproat
tonight for a tuck-in... she keeps asking for
you...

ABBY

I'm with my family tonight for a change. Do
not call me.

She clicks off the phone. The bus is in the distance and approaches. The older woman is kindly and looks at her with concern. Abby takes a few deep breaths and sits on the bench in the shelter.

WOMAN

Are you okay love?

ABBY

No... I'm not. [Pulls up her sleeve] Look at the scratch marks... poor old soul was beside herself... I cleaned her up as best I could... [getting upset] I had to leave her like that... all curled... you have no idea what goes on...

WOMAN

You did your best...

ABBY

I've only got one rule for myself... 'What if it was my mother?'

The bus pulls up. The woman moves to it.

WOMAN

Are you getting on?

Abby shakes her head and glances at her watch.

ABBY

No... I'm just killing time.

21. OPEN COUNTRYSIDE

The van is parked in a lay-by. Ricky and Liza Jane look out over gentle hills, a river below, and animals in the field. A beautiful quiet moment apart from the bird sound. No traffic. Bliss. They share a sandwich. Liza Jane notices Ricky smiling to himself.

> LIZA JANE
>
> What is it?

> RICKY
>
> Just got paid... feeling flush... [Liza Jane smiles too] Mum's off tonight... let's get a big giant Indian takeaway tonight.

> LIZA JANE
>
> Oh yes!

> RICKY
>
> Can use your tips?

> LIZA JANE
>
> Oh no!

> RICKY
>
> Phone Seb for me... ask him what he wants... persuade him to stay in darling... [glancing across at her] can you do that?

> LIZA JANE
>
> I wish you didn't fight so much.

Ricky looks at her for a moment, remorse in his eye. Silence for several long moments.

> LIZA JANE (CONT'D)
>
> Thanks for a great day Dad... can we do it again?

He squeezes her hand and nods. The gun bleeps from the van and they both hear it.

LIZA JANE (CONT'D)
The two minute bleep…

Ricky just nods as he stares out at the fields and horizon beyond.

22. HOME – SATURDAY NIGHT

Lots of laughter around the kitchen table as the whole family pounces on the takeaway dishes.

ABBY
Worse than piranha fish!

LIZA JANE
Seb… don't eat all the korma!

Seb is starving and dives in.

SEB
Delicious…

Ricky and Abby catch each other's eye for a second in the middle of the fun, and they are both so chuffed to see Seb in good form. He tries another and holds his mouth.

SEB (CONT'D)
Oh my God! So hot! What's that?

RICKY
[Chuckling] Vindaloo… sort out the men
from the boys…

He confidently takes a big mouthful himself and nearly chokes.

RICKY (CONT'D)
Ah Jesus Christ!

They all burst out laughing.

ABBY
Idiot… you'll kill yourself!

Abby's face beams, as she enjoys them all together.

ABBY (CONT'D)
Do you know there is something called an
'infinity chilli'… Two hundred times hotter
than normal.

RICKY
The chefs have got to wear goggles to cook
it… honestly.

They laugh.

LIZA JANE
Stop fibbing Dad…

Abby receives a text on her phone. She has a quick glance as the
others keep eating.

SEB
[Mock row] No mobiles at the table.

Liza Jane giggles.

RICKY
Can make you hallucinate… cause your
tongue to blister…

                              SEB
        Imagine the farts from that... burn a hole in
        your pants!

Liza Jane giggles. Seb grabs an entire naan bread. He eats like
only a teenager can. Ricky nudges Liza Jane to have a look at
her brother.

                           LIZA JANE
        Disss-gusting!

Seb looks up and catches them staring at him. He lets out a big
beaming smile, like his old self.

                              SEB
        This is so so so good... thanks Dad.

Ricky catches Abby's eye. The life has gone out of her. She
moves over to the sink for a glass of water, but glances at the
phone again. She comes back and sits down.

                            RICKY
        What's up Abby?

Silence for a moment.

                             ABBY
        It's Mollie... one of the old folks... she was at
        a wedding... the taxi dropped her off... the
        family thought a carer was coming ... she's
        in a wheelchair and can't get into bed on her
        own... nothing organised for her...

                            RICKY
        Can they not phone the family?

ABBY

No answer… they tried.

RICKY

Have they not got anyone on call?

ABBY

You know what they're like… they've tried
other carers… she's been sitting there three
hours already… won't be the first time they've
left someone sitting up all night…

SEB

That's not right…

Ricky's frustration mounts.

ABBY

I can't leave her… I won't sleep.

RICKY

That's how these bastards get away with it!

ABBY

I'm going to get a taxi…

RICKY

On a Saturday night? You'll wait for hours…
[Wiping his mouth with a napkin] Let's get it
over with.

Ricky jumps up.

ABBY

[Trying to control her upset] I don't want to
spoil the fun… I'll get a taxi… I mean it! I'm
so sorry…

She catches Seb's eye. Seb stands up and walks round behind her.

> SEB
>
> Come on! We'll all go! Can't we Dad?
> [Winking at Ricky, drawing him in] We can
> feed the old girl some of that vindaloo and
> she'll be up doing press-ups.

> ABBY
>
> I'm so sorry...

> SEB
>
> Come on! It'll be a laugh, squeezed in! Put on
> some music.

> LIZA JANE
>
> Yeah... altogether!

> SEB
>
> [Cuddling her in a bear hug] We can double
> buckle... but you'll have to sit on my knee
> Mum!

Abby can feel her eyes well up and has to turn away.

23. MOLLIE'S STREETS AND FLAT

OUTSIDE: the van drives through nearby streets, music pumping out. It pulls up near Mollie's flat. As Abby leaves, Liza Jane opens the window.

> LIZA JANE
>
> We're fine here Mum... so don't rush...

She catches sight of Ricky laugh at something Seb must have said, and appreciates the fun between them; the simple joys. She walks across to the front door, finds the key and lets herself in.

INSIDE: Abby steps into the sitting room. Mollie sits there by a side light, and looks up. She is in her best clothes but desperately sad.

                    MOLLIE
          On a Saturday night… I'm sorry Abby… I'm
          so sorry sweetheart…

Abby kneels down before her and takes her hand.

                    ABBY
          It's me that's sorry… how long have you been
          waiting?

Mollie shakes her head.

                    ABBY (CONT'D)
          You look bloody gorgeous! Hope you had a
          drink.

                    MOLLIE
          One too many… never made it on time.

A moment between them.

                    ABBY
          I'll get a pad and get you tidied up and tucked
          in.

                    MOLLIE
          So humiliating.

                    ABBY
          Mollie… don't you ever forget this… look at
          me… [taking her hand] look at me… [at last
          she does]… you give me more than you will
          ever know.

24. HOME – NIGHT

LATER THAT NIGHT: Ricky and Abby's bedroom. They cuddle up to each other in bed.

>   ABBY
> They surprise you sometimes… just when
> you don't expect it… he was back to his old
> self, funny, gentle, full of fun. [Feeling it] Oh
> God… if this goes on I'm scared the school
> will kick him out…

>   RICKY
> Kills me… always hoped he'd be the first of
> our family to go to uni… [Pause] Tried to ask
> him if there was problem with a teacher… or
> bullying… just froze up on me… nothing.

She nods.

>   ABBY
> I've got to cut these hours… three nights back
> isn't enough… they need us home.

They hold eyes for a moment and Ricky gently kisses her.

>   RICKY
> You smell of Vick…

>   ABBY
> Try to wash it off… I put it on my top lip…
> keep the smell away…

>   RICKY
> Thank you.

She chuckles.

                              ABBY
        Eeejit.

                              RICKY
        My hands... smell of plastic and cardboard...

                              ABBY
        Hey... we could start a new line in
        perfumes... Abby's Minty Vick, Ricky's
        Mouldy Cardboard...

Eye to eye for a long moment.

                              RICKY
        I didn't think it would be this hard. It doesn't
        seem right does it? Everything seems...
        [struggling for right words]... out of whack.

                              ABBY
        [She touches his cheek] I keep getting this
        dream... we're both stuck in quicksand... just
        me and you... the kids are trying to reach us
        with a branch... [pause] feels like the harder
        we work... the more we sink...

Long moment between them. Ricky gives her another little
kiss, testing.

                         ABBY (CONT'D)
        Sorry Ricky... don't know what's wrong with
        me... if we make love... I think I might not
        stop crying for a week... let's try tomorrow
        when I get back a bit earlier... [touching his
        cheek] Is that okay?

                    RICKY

An appointment…

                    ABBY

Yeah… an appointment.

They smile, and cuddle in.

25. TOWER BLOCK (WITH RICKY) AND BUS STOP (WITH ABBY)

Ricky jogs to a tower block with parcel and HHD. He listens on the phone as he runs along. He enters the tower block.

26. STREET OF SHOPS

Abby is at a bus stop.

                    ABBY

There's an emergency meeting tonight at the school.

                    RICKY

Tonight! Some bloody notice that!

                    ABBY

Been organised since last week… Seb hid the letter… and I missed some lost calls… It's with the headmaster, welfare officer, and his year teacher… they want to see us both with Seb.

                    RICKY

What's the rush?

                    ABBY

He had a fight on Friday… a teacher tried to

                        96

stop it… Seb shoved him and he fell over and
hurt his wrist… Seb lost it… went crazy…

RICKY

Shit…

ABBY

It's a serious meeting Ricky…

25. CONTINUED: INSIDE TOWER BLOCK

Ricky confronts the lift 'Out of Order' sign and slaps the lift
in frustration. He runs to the intercom and presses a button for
floor 6.

RICKY

[Checking his HHD] Jesus… I've still got
forty-two deliveries Abby… and SEVEN
PRECISERS… can't get anyone to cover me
now…

ABBY

He could be suspended…

A voice from the intercom.

VOICE

Who is it?

RICKY

Delivery for Mr Davis… It's your mobile sir…
can you please have photographic proof of
identity…

VOICE

Don't worry mate… I'll look for it…

RICKY

[Frustration] You must have got a text
explaining sir... I'm up against the clock so
please have it ready... [Letting go of button]
You fucking dickhead!

He starts jogging up the stairs, talking to Abby on the phone.

RICKY (CONT'D)
I'll try my very best, Abby...

ABBY

I'm nervous Ricky... the headmaster was so
sharp last time...

RICKY
Abby! I said I would try! What else can I do?!

ABBY

I don't want to go on my own...

RICKY

I said I'd try my fucking best! Sorry... [She
cuts him off] Fuck! Fuck!

He knocks on the door and a tough looking character answers.
He tries to grab the package but Ricky pulls it back.

RICKY (CONT'D)
Photo identity please sir.

MAN

Can't find it... come on... give me a break
mate.

RICKY

Passport or driving licence, or other
photographic…

MAN

[Trying to grab it again] Fuck that man… I
paid for it and I want my fucking phone…

He grabs Ricky's arm.

RICKY

I don't want problems sir… please.

MAN

Give me the fucking phone man! I need my
phone!!! Three days without it and I need it
now!!! Hand it over! Two hundred quid it cost
me!

RICKY

Sorry sir… but it's my job…

MAN

[Rougher] Fuck your job! Loser!

Ricky hardly realises it himself, but in a flash he has the man up
against the wall by the throat so hard the man's eyes are bulging,
and he can't utter a word, never mind take a breath.

RICKY

[Quietly] Fuck my job… means fuck my
family.

He lets him go and the man doubles up.

26. CONTINUED. STREET OF SHOPS

Abby bustles out of a chemist's already on the phone.

                    ABBY
        Eddy... it's me, Abby. Just picked up your new
        prescription... running twenty minutes late...
        I'll be up as fast as I can.

An old voice answers.

                    EDDY
        Thank you Abby... that's really kind of you.

Abby walks at speed. Another call, straight to answering
machine.

                    ABBY
        [Breathing heavily with the pace] Seb... did
        you get my text? [Heavy] You better be at the
        school on time... I really mean it! Phone me
        back.

She phones again. Another answering machine.

                    ABBY (CONT'D)
        Liza darling... something's come up. Jessie's
        mum, she'll pick you up for swimming
        okay... all your gear's in the sports bag... pasta
        in the tupper... and NO computer before
        homework... I've signed the permission
        form for the school trip and money in the
        envelope... something else... damn, can't
        remember... Love you.

She walks on, at a firm pace, sweat on her brow, obviously under
stress, as she checks more texts coming in after several bleeps.

27. DEPOT – EVENING

Ricky, sweating, runs into the depot and slots his HHD into the correct spot for overnight charging.

Next he rushes to drop off his returns (the parcels he couldn't deliver or leave in a safe space) into a cage.

Maloney appears on stairs above him. He is on his mobile.

> MALONEY
> [Quick aside on the phone] Ricky... you got
> a moment?

> RICKY
> I'm in a terrible rush mate... late for a school
> meeting...

Maloney nods at him, but continues talking on the phone. Ricky tries to control his impatience; he attracts Maloney's attention and points at his watch.

> MALONEY
> [To listener on the phone] Give me a sec...
> [To Ricky, concerned] It's okay... you're
> doing great, hitting your figures... good
> feedback...

> RICKY
> Thanks, got to rush.

> MALONEY
> Just one thing... did you have anyone with
> you on the run on Saturday?

                          RICKY
Liza Jane... my ten-year-old.

                        MALONEY
Sorry... we can't have that...

                          RICKY
My van, my insurance, my daughter...
thought it was my business?

                        MALONEY
But our franchise... complaint from a
client... nobody fucks with them, ever... first
commandment. Okay?

Maloney steps away again, continuing his conversation, joking on
the phone. Ricky stares at him for a second, before running off.

28. STREET TO SCHOOL – EVENING

The van bombs towards the school at excessive speed. A janitor
is in the process of pulling the gate closed and locking up. Ricky
screeches to a halt. The janitor is wary, given the speed of the
van. Ricky winds the window down.

                          RICKY
I've got a meeting with the headmaster
mate... with my wife and son...

                        JANITOR
It's all closed up.

                          RICKY
Is there another entrance... maybe they're still
there?

                            103

> JANITOR
>
> I've locked the whole school… too late.

The janitor walks off. Ricky winds up the window and sits back in his seat exhausted. He snaps in the silence of his own cabin.

> RICKY
>
> Fuck! Fuck! Fuck! Fuck!!!!!!!!!

29. HOME, LIVING ROOM – NIGHT

Ricky, Abby and Seb are in the living room, with Seb trying his best to ignore them. It is late, and tempers are frayed after a tough day. Ricky is trying to make sense of the letter in his hand, as Seb stares at the table in wilful silence.

> RICKY
>
> [Reading] I realise that this exclusion may well be upsetting for you and the whole family… [he glances up at Seb] but there must be clear consequences for violent behaviour. Your son is banned from being in any public space during school hours, and should work from home… [Ricky, frustrated, looks up at Abby and Seb] Home?! How is he going to work at home?!… [Back to reading]… Using an online learning programme called SAM, with logging-on details as below… what a fucking joke…

Ricky catches a semi-smirk on Seb's face.

> RICKY (CONT'D)
>
> When Harpoon got done he was suspended from classes but had to go to the school library under supervision… is that right?

Seb just stares at the table.

                    RICKY (CONT'D)
          Did you hear me?

Still no answer.

                    RICKY (CONT'D)
          [To Abby] Did you ask about that?

                    ABBY
          I was too nervous Ricky... he was
          complaining about you not being there...

                    RICKY
          There's no way he'll study at home... can we
          get it changed to supervision at the school?

Abby's frustration mounts at the tone. Silence as he waits for
an answer.

                    RICKY (CONT'D)
          Abby?

                    ABBY
          I don't know.

                    RICKY
          Just common sense... first obvious question.

                    ABBY
          Why don't you phone him and ask?

                    RICKY
          Why didn't you ask him when you were face
          to face? Can't believe you didn't...

ABBY

Why didn't you turn up on time and ask all
the smart questions yourself?!

RICKY

Because I was running round like a blue-arsed
fly... not even time to eat a sandwich! Not
one bite!

ABBY

I had to beg to get a replacement...
humiliating. Think you're the only one with
a tough job? At least you have transport... I
was stuck at freezing bus stops getting bawled
at for being late... I'm sick to the back teeth of
you all!

Abby jumps up and leaves. Silence. Ricky stares at Seb who
continues to stare at the table. He gives away nothing.

RICKY

The only time... the only time ever... I argue
with your mum... it's about you.

SEB

Yeah Dad... it's always my fault.

This time Seb holds his eye, without a flicker.

30. ROSIE'S HOUSE

Abby is back again with Rosie. (The old lady that previously
swiped the food from the table. Abby has done a deal with Rosie,
that if she allows Rosie to comb her hair, she has to finish her
soup.)

Abby kneels before Rosie, so Rosie can comfortably comb Abby's hair. Clear it gives Rosie profound satisfaction, and has totally changed her temper. She does it gently and tenderly with an old quality brush she used for her own daughter decades ago. As she brushes she sings in a tuneful voice. (A traditional song that became well known in the 30's, 'Irene, Goodnight'.)

> ROSIE
> Irene goodnight Irene, Irene goodnight,
> goodnight Irene, goodnight Irene, I'll see you
> in my dreams...

As she brushes she sometimes looks into Abby's eyes as if she can see right inside her.

> ROSIE (CONT'D)
> Quit your ramblin', quit your gamblin', stop
> staying out late at night, go home with your
> kids and family, stay there by the fireside
> bright...

For a moment she lays her hand on Abby's cheek.

> ROSIE (CONT'D)
> Sometimes I live in the country, sometimes
> I live in the town, sometimes I take a great
> notion, to jump in the river and drown...

Rosie continues to hold her eye, gently brushing as Rosie goes back to the chorus.

> ROSIE (CONT'D)
> Irene goodnight Irene, Irene goodnight,
> goodnight Irene, goodnight Irene, I'll see you
> in my dreams...

She stops for a moment.

ROSIE (CONT'D)
[Eye to eye] Is your heart broken sweetheart?

ABBY
I think it is Rosie...

ROSIE
Don't fret darling... I'll brush all your pains
away...

She begins the song again as Abby weeps, safe, in gentle old
hands.

ROSIE (CONT'D)
Irene goodnight Irene, Irene goodnight...

31. DEPOT: MALONEY'S OFFICE

Ricky sits in front of Maloney's desk which is covered in papers.
Maloney just stares at Ricky as he speaks.

RICKY
You know I'm a grafter... no bullshit from
me... but things are a bit [pause] rocky at
home... trouble with a teenage boy... driving
us round the bend... skipping school... he's
on the war path... even the wee one's not
sleeping properly now... she's ten... it's all
getting my wife Abby down... sorry to ask
this... I just need a week off... one week...
spend a bit of time with them... talk it
through... with the commute I seldom get
back before nine... never together when we're
not all knackered...

MALONEY

Why ask me? Don't need to beg favours... just
organise a replacement driver... you won't pay
a penny... your business... remember?

Ricky squirms in his seat.

RICKY

I've tried at least eight mates... people I
know that could do the job and not fuck you
about... no luck... I can maybe get a lad after
Christmas... I've spoken to the drivers here
too... we all chip in... hire an extra driver
among half a dozen of us... give us a bit of
breathing space.

Maloney lets Ricky squirm. He just waits for the answer.

RICKY (CONT'D)
They're going to think about it...

MALONEY

Excellent... plan ahead, initiative...

RICKY

Ah Jesus... I need a week now! So I'm
asking you the enormous favour... let me
off a week... just five days even... Abby's
struggling... had the baby blues when Liza
Jane was born... scared she goes down
again...

MALONEY

I had four drivers in here last week... Driver
A... on his mate's sofa... his wife kicked him

out... Driver B... his sister had a stroke...
Driver C, fucking piles, I kid you not, needs
an operation... Driver D, his daughter ...
attempted suicide... could go on all day. Every
family... at some point... has a problem... it
is called life... my old man was a farmer...
milked cows... did he ever have a day off?

RICKY

Three days... I promise... that's all I'm
asking...

MALONEY

Everybody in this building knows I am Nasty
Bastard No. 1... but greatly misunderstood...
all the complaints, the anger, the fury, the
hatred... I soak it all up, use it for fuel... and
with all the energy I form a protective shield
around our depot... [pointing to the graphs
and figures stuck to his wall]... the depot
with the best figures in the whole country bar
none... that means a shield around my drivers,
your families... know why I am number one?
[He taps his nails on a HHD] I keep the wee
black box happy... this little bastard is worse
than a shark... all those doors you knock on...
all those faces... has there ever been anyone
who asked how you are? Don't give a shit if
you fall asleep and smack a bus head on... all
they care about is price, delivery... thing in
the hand... all that gets fed into the wee black
box... that wee black box is in competition
with all the other black boxes... that decides
the contracts, who lives, who dies... I want
Amazon here, Apple here, Samsung, Zara, all

here for my drivers, your families… it may
just look like shit… but this depot is a fucking
gold mine… shareholders should erect a statue
in the car park… of me, Maloney… Patron
Saint Of Nasty Bastards. You want a day off…
it will cost you two hundred fucking quid a
go.

FADE.

32. DEPOT – EARLY MORNING

Outside, the vans drive away, one by one. Inside, Maloney,
highly agitated after late arrival of the supplying lorry, is now
trying to get the loaded-up vans out as fast as possible.

Ricky and Henry's vans are in the far away corner and will be
among the last to leave. Ricky finishes off laying in his last parcel
and slams the back door shut. Just as he does so he gets a call and
answers the phone which doesn't please Maloney.

MALONEY
Come on… time to make up! Out of here!

Henry, getting ready to get into his own van, watches the body
language of Ricky change.

RICKY
What?!! Is this a wind up? Where is he? Can I
speak to him? No… I can't come now… I am
right in the middle of a shift… Sorry… I can't
come… Ah Christ!!! Let me phone my wife…
I'll see if she can make it, but she's at work
too… I'll get back to you in a minute… thank
you officer… I'll phone right back…

HENRY

What's wrong mate?

RICKY

[Dialling] That stupid dick!!!!! Come on
Abby… answer the fucking phone for Christ's
sake…

Maloney is watching the drama, and already showing impatience.
The vans beside him are pulling out.

HENRY

What's wrong Ricky?

RICKY

Seb's just been arrested… fucking caught
shoplifting… the cop's a decent guy… first
offence… trying to avoid charging him…
but he needs a parent there… Abby for fuck's
sake!!! Answer the phone… [to Henry] if he
gets a criminal record…

Ricky tries to take a deep breath.

MALONEY

What the fuck is going on here?

RICKY

[To answering machine] Abby… phone me
now… now! It's really urgent!! [To Maloney]
I'm really sorry… emergency back home…
can you give me a minute…

MALONEY

Shit! [Checking his watch] Two hours behind
schedule with the broken down lorry from

112

Manchester… my stats all to fuck! You have
sixty seconds!

Ricky is dialling again.

> RICKY
> Sorry officer… I'm trying to get my wife…
> no answer… [Listening] Ah Christ… [He
> stares at the vans leaving, then at Maloney]
> I'm right in the middle of chaos here… [Deep
> breaths, growing panic, to Henry, hand over
> the phone]… Ah fuck… what will I do?

> HENRY
> You better go…

Ricky looks at a loss, rabbit in the headlights. He has to make
a decision.

> RICKY
> [To police] Okay okay okay…

> MALONEY
> One minute up!

> RICKY
> I'm sorry… I've got to go home.

> MALONEY
> Holy Fuck!!!! How am I supposed to get a
> driver now?! [All bar Henry have left] Can't
> even share the parcels!

> RICKY
> I'm sorry… something personal… I'll tell you
> later…

MALONEY

Personal?! Think I'm a fucking counsellor?!!
Get the parcels out of your van and that's you
with a sanction! Personal my arse! You had
seven PRECISERS! Seven! Fuck!!

He storms off and boots an empty cardboard box.

MALONEY (CONT'D)

[Turning] You'll pay through the fucking
nose for this!

Henry, helping Ricky unpack his van, hurls the parcels to Ricky
at speed who lays them down on the floor. He looks humiliated.

33. POLICE STATION

Seb and Ricky sit opposite each other at a table, with a uniformed
officer at the head. He is mature, with bite. He has a file of papers
before him.

POLICEMAN

In your favour you have been honest and
admitted what happened. After this you will
sign a form accepting the circumstances of
the caution. It will be recorded on the Police
National Computer...

RICKY

Does that mean it's a conviction?

POLICEMAN

No it's not... but it may be used in future
criminal proceedings as evidence of
character... [To Seb] Do you understand?

114

Seb stares at his hands.

POLICEMAN (CONT'D)

[Sharply] I said do you understand?

SEB

Yes.

POLICEMAN

[Sharp again] Sit up properly... [Seb
straightens up a bit.] This is a big moment...
some take this as a red warning and are never
in trouble again... others follow a pattern of
further offences which will blight the rest
of their lives... their work, study, travel,
mortgage, rent, insurance, you name it...
I've seen it all before... [pause] the biggest
indicator of which track you will take often
reflects your parents... [He refuses to look up
from the table]... Your father has made an
enormous effort to be here today... I hope, for
all your sakes, you learn the lesson. Do you
think you will?

Seb stubbornly stares at the table. A glance between Ricky and
the policeman.

LIVING ROOM: Ricky and Abby confront Seb, who is
fidgeting with his mobile.

RICKY

Would you mind putting the phone away...

He continues to answer the text at speed.

I'm listening… [still texting]… called…
multitasking…

RICKY

I won't ask again…

SEB

I bet you do.

ABBY

Seb! Cut it out!

He continues. Seb puts it away a millisecond before Ricky is
about to snap. He looks up at them.

SEB

All ears…

RICKY

Has the penny dropped… what a conviction
means?

At her bedroom door, Liza Jane, clearly anxious, listens to the
raised voices from the living room.

SEB

Fuck's sake! Boys out there stealing motor
bikes… carrying knives… selling drugs… I
lifted three shitty cans of paint… less than
fifteen quid!

Back to the living room.

RICKY

We don't steal in this family!

                    SEB
It was a chain store… not a corner shop.

                    ABBY
So that makes it okay Seb… what next?

                    SEB
Mass murder I suppose…

                    RICKY
Every course you apply for… every job…
every form you fill in…

Seb gets another text and starts reading it. Ricky takes a deep
breath and Abby holds his arm.

                RICKY (CONT'D)
Do you know how much that cost us today?

                    SEB
Didn't ask you to come.

                    RICKY
Two hundred for a replacement driver… plus
my day's work… plus a sanction… a fortune
you cost the family…

There is no response as he flicks through more messages.

                RICKY (CONT'D)
Does that mean anything to you?

                    ABBY
Put the phone away!

Seb quickly does a short text. Ricky's fury mounts.

> RICKY
> Your mother's speaking to you!

> SEB
> Calm down... all this stress...

> RICKY
> Things are going to change round here! First
> thing, you're going to school... every single
> day, without exception!

> SEB
> And how are you going to do that Dad? Put
> me in a straitjacket?

> RICKY
> You are going to school... had it up to here!

> SEB
> Ah... got it... [smirking]... parcel me up,
> throw me in the back of your van, special
> delivery!

Ricky snaps the phone from his hands.

> RICKY
> You'll get your phone back if you go to
> school!

Seb explodes. He jumps up and screams at Ricky.

> SEB
> Give me my phone!!!

Ricky and Abby are taken aback by the ferocity. Seb tries to wrestle it back.

SEB (CONT'D)
Give me my fucking phone!!!!

He really goes at Ricky pushing him up against the wall. Trying to snatch back the phone. He is almost hysterical. Abby tries to get in between them. Ricky has stuck it in his pocket and holds Seb back at a distance. It takes all his strength.

RICKY
Stand back! I'm warning you!!

SEB
Give me my fucking phone!! Now!!

He still comes at him, ramming Ricky up against the wall.

RICKY
Back off now!!

Liza Jane bursts in upset. She jumps in between them.

LIZA JANE
Stop it stop it stop stop stop it!!!!!! I can't stand it!!

It stuns them all.

SEB
Biggest mistake of your life… you're going to fucking pay!

Seb bursts out of the room, as Abby bends down to cuddle Liza Jane. Noise of the front door slamming as Seb storms out from the house.

                    ABBY

It's okay darling, it's okay.

                  LIZA JANE

It's not okay… not okay.

Ricky tries to lay a hand on her shoulder but she shrugs it off.

LATER: IN THEIR BEDROOM: Abby and Ricky are both
deeply upset.

                    ABBY

We have to learn to wind it down… not wind
it up…

                   RICKY

So it's my fault he won't go to school?
Shoplifting… and now six hundred quid!
Selfish wee shit!

                    ABBY

Ricky… we're on to something else… way
beyond being right or wrong…

                   RICKY

Bollocks! That's what it is… right or wrong!

                    ABBY

I've seen it with my friends' boys… We've just
got to keep… connected with him… keep in
touch… and hope we get through it…

                   RICKY

We keep connected! You've got to back me
up or we're done for!

ABBY

We're done for if you don't watch yourself!
You have a temper on you… and you're
exhausted.

RICKY

All my fucking fault!

ABBY

If you raise a hand… there's a before and
after… never the same… that could have
turned to blows… it was that close… Oh
God, look at my father…

RICKY

For Christ's sake! That's below the belt. I'm
not like that old bastard!

ABBY

Things can get out of hand… before you
know it… I've seen it…

RICKY

What are you saying Abby?

ABBY

I couldn't live with that…

RICKY

If you think I'm like him, you know what to
do about it?! Fuck off and pack your bags!

LIZA JANE

[Screaming from outside] Daddy! Stop it!!
Stop it!! Stop it!!! Don't go Mum! Stop
fighting!!

It knocks them for six. Abby heads through to calm Liza Jane. Ricky slumps to a sitting position on the bed, with Seb's phone still in his hand. He can hear Abby's whispers and Liza Jane's sobs. It's torture for him. Seb's phone starts ringing. Ricky is unsure, and stares at it. It's a relief when it goes to answerphone. Then a ping of a text coming in.

> RICKY
> [To himself] Oh Christ…

At last Abby comes back.

> RICKY (CONT'D)
> I'm sorry Abby…

> ABBY
> I didn't tell you before… didn't want to worry you… but she's wetting the bed.

He can hardly believe it.

> RICKY
> Ah Christ… is she wet now?

> ABBY
> No… but I promised to sleep with her… she's trembling the wee soul.

Ricky is done in, and has no words. Abby sees him fidget nervously with Seb's phone. Ricky feels the weight of the phone in his hand, and looks up at Abby like a lost boy.

> ABBY (CONT'D)
> We have to pick our battles… he's so angry… let's take a deep breath and see if we can get through this…

RICKY

I don't know what to do Abby.

ABBY

The phone... all his mates... his network...
photos of his paintings... even his homework
is on there Ricky, did you know that?

Another blow. Ricky shakes his head.

ABBY (CONT'D)

It's his whole life... what do we gain by
cutting him off? [Long pause] Give me the
phone Ricky... I'll talk to him when he
comes back... calm him down... try and get
him back to school... [pause] underneath, he's
a good boy...

Ricky lets out a long sigh and hands the phone to her.

RICKY

Should I go and look for him?

Abby shakes her head.

ABBY

He'll be at Harpoon's... I'll text him now.

Abby grabs her night dress and heads to the door to join Liza
Jane.

RICKY

What are we doing to each other?

Abby stops for a moment at the door. She looks done in too.

ABBY

I don't know Ricky... I don't know.

She closes the door, as a cold shiver runs through him.

LATER: Liza Jane lies in her bed, an uneasiness in her as she turns in the middle of the night. Abby is curled up beside her, fast asleep. Liza Jane hears a strange noise outside in the hall.

Familiar. The shaking of a spray paint can, and then the spraying. She stirs, and gets up. She moves out into the landing. Seb is at the bottom of the stairs. She leans over and catches a glimpse of him as he disappears below. She stares at the photographs (seen earlier with Mollie) on the wall halfway down the stairs. The images with Ricky and Seb have an 'X' sprayed over them, which spreads out over the wall. The disfigurement over smiling faces shocks her deeply. She runs down the stairs, opens the front door and looks out. No sign of Seb.

35. HOME – NEXT MORNING

Liza Jane lies in her bed, by herself, and cuddles into her soft elephant as she hears the chaos outside her door. She hums gently to her toy.

RICKY'S VOICE

Look at the photos... paint all over the wall!

ABBY'S VOICE

He's not in his room... taken his rucksack.

RICKY'S VOICE

The keys to the van have gone too... both sets! Fuck!!

ABBY

He hasn't taken the van... don't tell me that!

IN THE HALLWAY: Ricky and Abby rush to the front door and open it. They are relieved to see the van there, but, written with a finger, on the dirty side of the van is one word, with an exclamation mark: 'Prick!'

> RICKY
>
> He's taken my keys…

> ABBY
>
> Have you checked your pockets?

He does so, and then the floor under the shelf where the keys normally are.

> RICKY
>
> Phone him…

Abby gives him a look.

> RICKY (CONT'D)
>
> Ah shit…

> ABBY
>
> I'll search his room again.

Abby runs up the stairs again to Seb's room. Ricky desperately tries all the pockets to the coats and jackets hanging by the door. Abby searches in Seb's room.

HALL BY THE DOOR: Growing panic as Ricky checks his watch. He climbs the stairs again to the landing.

> RICKY
>
> Jesus Christ… look at the time… they'll go
> crazy… Fuck!!

Abby's phone rings now too. Her face darkens.

                    ABBY
          [Answering] I'll be there as soon as I can...
          I'm sorry... I'm on my way...

Ricky looks beside himself.

                    ABBY (CONT'D)
          Ricky... I'm late...

                    RICKY
          Do we have the numbers of his mates?

                    ABBY
          Only Harpoon, but he won't pick up.

                    RICKY
          Ah Christ... what will I do Abby? If I phone
          Maloney will go crazy after yesterday...
          Fuck!!! Another two hundred quid fine... or
          maybe fire me... Ah Christ...

                    ABBY
          You know where Harpoon lives... Dodge
          too...

                    RICKY
          Look at the time!

                    ABBY
          You could take Seb's old bike? Cycle round...
          it'll be faster than waiting for a taxi at this
          time...

RICKY

    Wee bastard!!

His face fumes, but there is no option.

36. STREETS NEAR HOME

Comic, but tragic. The bike is too small for Ricky, and the seat
is stuck too low. He cycles as fast as he can, knees sticking out
to the side to manage the pedals. He pants up a hill as best he
can. He looks to his right and can see some workmen in a van
pissing themselves laughing as they overtake.

He talks to a sleepy Harpoon on the doorstep. The latter shakes
his head.

By the side of a road. Ricky has stopped. Traffic speeds past. He
is on the phone; done in, and defeated.

MALONEY'S VOICE
    Lost your fucking keys! Dog ate my
    homework! Zombies invade planet earth! Two
    days in a row, messed up my stats, you have
    just jumped from being a Blue Eyed Boy to
    Arsehole… two hundred quid and another
    sanction… next one, red card! Dickhead!

The phone goes dead.

37. HOME – EVENING

Ricky sits on the sofa, several cans of beer by his side, nursing his
wrath. He sits there, festering, staring into space. Reliving every
moment of injustice. The front door sounds, and he pounces. He
goes to the landing, beer can in his hand as Seb climbs the stairs.

RICKY

Where's my fucking keys?

SEB

Oh… lost your keys… what a shame.

Seb goes past Ricky into his bedroom.

RICKY

Give me the keys!

Seb faces him.

SEB

Give me my phone!!

RICKY

Last chance… give me the keys!

SEB

What are you talking about? [He flicks the
beer can with his finger, making a clunking
sound] Pissed old fart!

Ricky snaps. With full force, with the back of his fist, he punches
Seb smack in the jaw. It hurls him, crashing his head against the
wall. He collapses in a heap. Out cold.

Abby runs from the living room and pushes past Ricky. She
bends down over Seb. Blood trickles from his mouth.

ABBY

Ah Christ… what have you done?!

Ricky is frozen in shock.

ABBY (CONT'D)

Seb... are you okay?

RICKY

Oh Christ...

He comes to, his eyes flicker, but he is too groggy to speak.

RICKY (CONT'D)

Seb...

ABBY

Get out of my sight! You big brute! What did
I tell you?

Ricky stumbles out of the house.

Liza Jane stands at her bedroom door. No tears. Stuck to the spot.

38. PARK NEARBY – EVENING

Ricky just sits on the bench. Wretched. His eyes flick now and
then to a bunch of teenagers, messing around under a streetlamp
at another bench some distance away. Some are drinking, others
are on their phones. But it is their laughter that feeds his misery.
His phone rings. He hesitates. He answers.

LIZA JANE

Please come Dad... please...

RICKY

I need some time sweetheart... is your brother
okay?

LIZA JANE

He's just left... please come Dad... please,
right now.

39. HOME – EVENING

Ricky and Abby sit in the kitchen over a cup of tea. Liza Jane sits on Ricky's knee and he has his arms around her. Distraught. She fiddles with her toy elephant, her finger nervously digging into a hole in the body of the toy.

> ### LIZA JANE
> I was sitting on the staircase… I was all
> upset… wanted Seb back… wanted it the way
> it used to be… I thought if you just stayed at
> home Dad… if you just stayed at home…

She breaks again. Ricky cuddles her more tightly.

> ### ABBY
> It's okay darling… it's okay…

> ### RICKY
> What is it sweetheart? You can tell us.

She digs into the hole in her elephant and pulls out one set of keys for the van. She digs in again, and pulls out the other. Abby and Ricky can't believe their eyes.

> ### LIZA JANE
> I picked up the keys… hid them… [Rubbing
> her eyes] I thought if you stayed at home
> Dad… but when all the shouting started… I
> got so scared… I tried to tell you… I wanted
> to…

She is breaking her heart now in deep sobs.

> ### ABBY
> You just froze darling.

She nods vigorously.

LIZA JANE

It wasn't Seb... it was me.

Ricky cuddles her tight and kisses the top of her head.

LIZA JANE (CONT'D)

It's all my fault... we've got to tell Seb... I
want him back... want him back now...

Ricky and Abby look at each other over the top of Liza Jane.
They are still stunned. Ricky is even more godforsaken.

RICKY

Not your fault darling... I'm so so sorry.

Abby leans over and takes both her hands.

ABBY

Don't fret darling... he's with Harpoon...
I've talked to his mum and she's lovely... he's
safe and he's fine... [to Liza Jane] you can call
him... he's got his phone back... do you want
to do that?

Through her tears she nods.

LIZA JANE

But when is he coming home?

ABBY

Soon darling... when things calm down.

LIZA JANE

I've got to tell him it's my fault. I want to tell
him now... and I really miss him.

FADE.

40. COUNTRY ROAD

Ricky drives along. His eyes are droopy. More droopy yet. His shoulders drop. His head begins to nod, and he fights the sleep. Back to the road, mesmerizing. The hum of traffic. He approaches roadworks with traffic reduced to one lane controlled by temporary traffic lights. His head begins to nod again. His eyes close.

Amber. Red. Ricky wakes with a jolt and screams on the brakes. The van skids and nearly smashes into the stationary car in front, swerving to avoid it by inches. A car coming the other way breaks and swerves too to avoid him. Ricky's face turns pale.

> RICKY
>
> Holy fuck...

Pounding of horns from several cars whose drivers have been infuriated by the narrow escape.

Once he is safe Ricky pulls up, parks awkwardly, two wheels up clumsily on the verge, and at an odd angle; a bit strange.

INSIDE THE VAN: Ricky looks different, subdued, devoid of his usual energy. He dials his phone.

> RICKY (CONT'D)
>
> Hi love... maybe we can go out for a meal on Sunday?

> ABBY
>
> Would love that... so much... sorry darling...
> got to rush... those idiots double booked me
> again... I'll call you after...

> RICKY
>
> Abby...

He stops.

> ABBY

What is it Ricky?

> RICKY

Sometimes… it feels as if… [short pause] it's
all just hanging by a thread…

> ABBY

What is darling?

> RICKY

My life… yours… I was looking today at all
the faces of the drivers… all our little lives…
hanging by a thread.

> ABBY

Are you okay Ricky?

Brief pause.

> RICKY

We're just 'the little people', aren't we?

> ABBY

Ricky… did something happen?

> RICKY

No… I'm fine. Fine fine. I'm missing you
Abby.

> ABBY

Me too darling…

The gun bleeps.

41. HOME, SEB'S BEDROOM – NIGHT

Ricky is in Seb's bedroom gently turning over one sketch after another. Seb has a decent eye, and sharp imagination. Some images have grotesque faces and odd questions beside them. 'Who says…?' Another full of mouths, many twisted, some have long serpent-like tongues with words through them 'YAP YAP YAP FUCKING YAP'. But all have energy that draws him in. More grotesque images, of half-men and half-robots being charged up by some monstrous machine. It moves him, imagining Seb's hand sketching at speed.

The door opens and Abby peeks in. She glances at the sketches too. Only the noise of pages turning. A moment between them both. Ricky looks round the room at the posters and a few typical teenage photos of Seb with his mates, and some too of his graffiti designs.

> RICKY
> There's a whole part of him… I don't even know…

42. TOWER BLOCK: CAR PARK

Ricky pulls up in a car park which serves a tower block. It is bleak and quite isolated. Ricky grabs an empty plastic bottle, and looks around him. He unlocks the back door and pulls both parts open to give him some privacy. He steps to the side, tight by the door, opens the bottle, undoes his zip, and with some satisfaction, after a long drive, pisses into the bottle. He zips up. He then picks up the gun which was in the back of the van.

Suddenly the door snaps back on him, crushing him violently to the knees as he is jammed between the door and the edge of the back of the van. As the door is pulled open he doubles up with the pain and he drops the HHD onto the ground. Three men are on him, raining down kicks and blows.

Ricky grabs a leg and yanks it high as one of the assailants goes flying. He grabs another and headbuts him, bursting his nose.

MAN 1
Bastard! Bastard!!

But the other whacks Ricky full on the face. Ricky fights back, flailing like a madman. It takes all three again to subdue him, and they are bloodied too.

Kicks and boots all round, and Ricky is much more than they bargained for. All receive hefty blows and boots. But three men attacking becomes too much. One boots Ricky in the stomach winding him while another knees him repeatedly in the ribs. Ricky collapses but struggles to get up.

MAN 2
Arsehole... what's it to you?! Not your
fucking gear!

Ricky tries to get up but his ribs are too painful and he can hardly see through swollen eyes. At last, he lies back, resigned to the robbery as he drifts between dizziness and consciousness.

MAN 3
Mad fucking prick!

Two limp into the back of the van throwing the parcels into the third's big plastic bags.

MAN 1
Grab all the small ones... that's the mobiles.

MAN 3
Come on... let's go! There's somebody by a
window...

MAN 2

[To Ricky] Fucker you... lost my tooth...

He notices the plastic bottle of piss lying on its side.

MAN 2 (CONT'D)

Dirty bastard...

He grabs it. He walks over to Ricky and boots him once more.

MAN 3

Come on...

MAN 2

Crawl in your own piss!

He enjoys the moment, holding up the bottle over Ricky, letting the piss splash from a height all over him. He notices the HHD lying on the ground beside Ricky, picks it up, and examines it briefly.

MAN 1

Do you want me to sign?

The others laugh. He drops it on the ground and smashes it with his heel.

43. HOSPITAL A&E

The area is packed. Ricky sits there with Abby, who is still in carer's uniform. Ricky's jeans are cut open, to reveal ugly wounds to his knees where he was jammed by the doors. His face is badly swollen and cut. Abby, dabbing with cotton wool, cleans up his knees with her own kit. A body goes whizzing past on a trolley with the emergency team.

RICKY

Poor sods...

ABBY

Just badly bruised... are the painkillers
kicking in? [Ricky nods]... It's your head
and ribs I'm worried about... and your eye...
[getting upset] so swollen Ricky.

RICKY

I can see fine...

She takes his right hand and examines it gently. It is badly
swollen too.

ABBY

And you could have burst a few knuckles.

RICKY

Worth it... the bastards.

ABBY

Ah Ricky... [laying a gentle hand on his lap,
whispered] you must have passed out... wet
yourself...

RICKY

We piss into bottles sometimes... they threw
that over me... at least it's my own...

Abby just looks at him for a long moment; it is the utter
humiliation of it that cuts deep. She has to turn her face away.
Her hand trembles slightly as she puts it to her mouth.

RICKY (CONT'D)
I'm fine sweetheart... Abby... [she tries to
contain herself]... see if you can find out how
long it will be... I'd rather go home...

ABBY
No way... not without an X-ray.

Abby goes over to the desk to enquire from a senior nurse. More
urgent cases pass on trolleys. Ricky looks around him at the still
full waiting room.

Abby returns.

ABBY (CONT'D)
[Nodding at a senior nurse] Could be here for
hours... [She lays her hand on Ricky's] Jacky
can stay the whole night with Liza Jane if
needs be...

RICKY
Don't want her to see me like this...

ABBY
She'll be so upset...

RICKY
Did you speak to Seb?

She hesitates.

RICKY (CONT'D)
What did he say?

ABBY
He froze up... think he's in shock...

Ricky's phone rings, and the name of caller appears.

RICKY
[To Abby] It's Maloney... the supervisor.

Abby moves in closer, sharing the speaker with Ricky, as she is
determined to listen.

MALONEY
Are you okay?

RICKY
Still waiting for an X-ray...

MALONEY
Well good luck... did you get your van back?

RICKY
Henry brought it round.

MALONEY
Okay... I've been on to the insurance
companies... good news there... we are
covered for all phones, a small fortune... in
fact, everything [pause] bar the passports...
there were two Ricky... sorry about that...

RICKY
What's that mean?

MALONEY
Two hundred and fifty pounds for each
passport... a bit of a blow... Five hundred
quid mate.

RICKY

[Incredulous] I've got to pay five hundred
quid for two passports...

ABBY

[Shocked, whispered] Can't believe it...

MALONEY

Have you got a replacement driver for
tomorrow?

Ricky is stunned.

RICKY

I'm in hospital! You're not going to hit me
with another two hundred quid?

MALONEY

I don't make the rules Ricky... I'm sorry...
but the stiff one is the gun...

ABBY

The what?!

RICKY

[To Abby] The Hand Held Device... they
smashed it.

MALONEY

You know that's a grand... we can do
instalments...

RICKY

A grand!

Abby can't contain herself, and snaps the phone from him.

RICKY (CONT'D)
Abby... give me the phone...

She stands up and has her hand up to back him off. She tries
to keep her voice low, but her fury overcomes her, and several
people are riveted.

ABBY
I'm Ricky's wife. You listen! His face was
pounded... like a jelly... covered in cuts and
bruises... could have broken ribs, one piercing
his lung for all you know... could even
be trauma to his brain... [looking at him,
struggling] don't know about his eye... his
fingers maybe broken too... and you have the
gall to threaten him with a fine, day after day?
Then a thousand pounds for your device!

MALONEY
Very sorry, but he's self-employed...

ABBY
I can't believe this... working a fourteen hour
day... six days a week... for you, for you!

MALONEY
For himself.

ABBY
Don't give me your fancy gobbledygook...
he's beaten up, delivering your parcels...
you just dump him, wash your hands... that
can't be right... [staring at Ricky's messed up

face]... do you want to finish him off? Send
him to an early grave?!

RICKY

Abby... please give me the phone...

MALONEY

I'm sorry... but if it was up to me...

ABBY

If it was up to me... I would burn your type
in hell! Greedy, two-faced parasites!

RICKY

Abby... give me the phone!

ABBY

Know what kills me...? How you get away
with it. I'm sick to my soul... to my heart and
soul... with you money grabbers... destroying
families. Fuck you!

Ricky can't believe Abby swearing.

ABBY (CONT'D)

[Losing it, bursting] Fuck you!! All of you!
All your care about is money! We've got a life
too! Fuck you!!

She cuts off the phone and stares out at the shocked faces. Total
silence. All eyes upon her. She is more shocked than anyone.

ABBY (CONT'D)

[Almost breaking, beside herself, to the faces,
gently again] I don't swear... It's not me...

I hate to swear… it's violent to swear…
[Looking at her uniform, aware of it] I'm a
carer… I care… that's what I do… I care for
people… I'm sorry… [She spots a woman with
a child] I'm very very sorry…

A long moment of silence as she's overwhelmed. Ricky struggles
up and puts an arm around her.

                    RICKY
[Quietly] We're going home Abby… let's go
home sweetheart…

                    ABBY
[Coming to, quietly] The X-rays.

                    RICKY
I'll come in the morning… please Abby…
please sweetheart…

                    ABBY
Promise me Ricky…

                    RICKY
I promise… we're going home darling…

A nurse approaches, concerned for her. She supports them both
towards the taxi rank.

44. HOME – NIGHT

BEDROOM: A little light from the street shines on Ricky's face.
He stares at the ceiling, wide awake. Abby sleeps beside him.
Ricky hears steps on the stairs, and then a slight noise outside
the door. He tenses, and tries to sit up. The door opens very
gently. Ricky looks at a figure in a hoodie. There is light now
from the hall.

SEB

[Whispered] Dad... are you okay?

RICKY

Ah Seb... I'm fine son... a bit shaky... [long
pause]... thanks... thanks for asking...

He stands there for a long moment.

SEB

Can I get you something... a tea, or a glass of
water?

RICKY

Got one here son...

Seb moves a bit closer and his eyes are getting used to the dark.
He can focus now on his face, peering in closer.

SEB

[Shock] Ah Christ Dad... what have they
done?

RICKY

Looks worse than it is... I'll be fine.

Ricky can see Seb struggle.

SEB

Ah Dad... what a mess...

RICKY

I'm okay Seb... you know how thick my skull
is.

But he is too shocked for jokes.

SEB

Ah Dad…

RICKY

On you go to bed son… I'll be fine.

SEB

I'll see you in the morning… call if you need
anything…

RICKY

Good to see you Seb… very good.

The door closes quietly. Ricky is overwhelmed.

45. HOME – EARLY MORNING

KITCHEN: Very early, 5am. Ricky looks even worse, his face
still swollen, and the bruises have spread over his face. An angry
cut is barely covered by a plaster. The kettle has nearly boiled.
Ricky digs out a cup and throws in a teabag; his right hand
is badly swollen and bruised. His hand shakes as he pours the
boiling water into the cup. As he waits for it to cool for a second
he finds a pen in top pocket and then looks around for a piece
of paper. A notebook is full of Liza's drawings, and the drawer
reveals nothing. He feels inside his jacket pockets. He checks the
back pocket of his trousers and finds a SORRY WE MISSED
YOU card, which is a bit crumpled up and doubled over. In the
section for comments underneath he struggles to write a few
words with painful fingers as he leans the card on the bench.
'Don't get mad Abby. I'll be fine. Love you, R.'

He lays it up leaning on the kettle so she can't miss it. He picks
up the mug to sip, but he has to grab it with both hands as his
hands tremble slightly. He takes a sip, but he has an intake of
breath from the pain in his ribs.

BY THE FRONT DOOR: Ricky limps down the last few steps. As gently as he can, he picks up the van keys from the shelf, but they are tangled up with house keys. As he tries to unpick them, a bunch crash to the floor. It sounds very loud in the deadly silence. Ricky hesitates for a second and then hears a rumble from a room. He unlocks the front door as quietly as he can manage. He leaves the house and walks to the van (parked on the far side opposite the house) hobbling as fast as he can.

As Ricky sticks the key into the ignition he hears a shout and spots Seb sprinting from the house towards him. (He is in pyjama bottoms and hoodie thrown on top.) Ricky just manages to lock all the doors with central locking a second before Seb pulls at the passenger door, closest to the house.

                    SEB
          [Highly distressed] Where are you going Dad?
          Open the window! I want to speak to you!

Seb sprints round the driver's side. He is stunned when he sees Ricky's face up close.

                    SEB (CONT'D)
          Fuck's sake Dad... look at you! You can't
          drive like that!

He pulls wildly at the locked door.

                    SEB (CONT'D)
          Open the window! Please Dad! Open the
          window now!

Ricky opens the window some two inches to speak to Seb.

                    RICKY
          Calm down Seb... I'm going for an X-ray.

SEB

At 5.30 in the morning!! Dad, open the door!

RICKY

I'll speak to you tonight son... I promise...
[begging]... please Seb... please.

SEB

Look at you! Dad... you're going to hurt
yourself or somebody else... Ah fuck... open
the window just for a minute.

Ricky is gently shaking his head. Seb pounds the window in
frustration.

RICKY

[Weary] Please son... listen... they were
going to hit us with a whole bunch of fines...
thousands. We could end up on the street...
[Shaking his head] I won't have that...

SEB

I'm sorry Dad... I didn't mean to get you
fined... I'll pay you back... every penny, I
promise... get out of the van...

RICKY

Not your fault son... let me go before your
mum wakes up.

Ricky turns on the ignition, which panics Seb even more. He
puts the van into gear and edges forward. Seb runs out in front
of the van.

SEB

[Screaming] Stop Dad!... I'll get a job too...
I'll do anything!

RICKY

Please Seb... in six months we'll get this
sorted... I promise...

SEB

You're not thinking straight!

RICKY

Got to go son...

SEB

Please Dad... open the door... you're going to
kill yourself!

RICKY

Move son...

SEB

[Desperate] I want you back Dad... the way
you were... I want you back!

RICKY

Out of my way...

He jolts forward, a little too sudden.

SEB

Stop!!! I'm not moving!!!

Abby in her dressing gown, and Liza Jane sprint from the house
now too. They join Seb, blocking his path. Neighbours peer
from windows.

ABBY/LIZA JANE

Ricky!!!!! Dad!!!! Stop! Please Ricky!! Get
out of the van!

Abby tries to get through to him, pleading with him, banging on the window too. Liza Jane is terrified as she sees Ricky's face.

LIZA JANE
What's wrong with Dad?! Who hurt Dad?!
Dad! Dad! What happened Dad?!

Liza Jane begins to lose it. Ricky can't bear her torment, rams the van into reverse, and drives at speed to the next junction some 35 yards up the road. They all sprint after him. Screaming. But he is too fast, and manages to change into first gear and accelerate down the perpendicular street a few seconds before they can block him off. In the mirror he can see Seb lead the charge to catch him. Abby, and then Liza Jane follow as fast as they can. He approaches the junction to the main road. A car in front of him waits for a space in the traffic. Ricky blares his horn as Seb gets closer. The car in front moves on. In seconds, Ricky spots his chance and accelerates into the main road.

Seb gives up and stops. Abby and then Liza Jane catch up with him. They huddle into each other, broken hearted, as they see the van disappear.

ABBY
Oh Ricky... oh darling...

LIZA JANE/SEB
Daddy... Daddy... Dad... Ah Dad...

VAN: Ricky drives on. His smartphone in the holder bleeps. One white van after another peppers the cold morning as the city wakes to another day.

FADE.

Ken Loach
Director

Where did the idea for *Sorry We Missed You* come from?
After we'd finished *I, Daniel Blake,* I was thinking, 'Well, maybe that's the last film.' But when we were going to the foodbanks for our research many of the people that were coming in were working – part time, zero-hour contracts. This is a new type of exploitation. The so-called gig economy, the self-employed or agency workers, the casualised workforce just continued to feature in mine and Paul's [Laverty] ongoing daily conversations. Gradually the idea emerged that maybe there was another film that might be worth making – not exactly a companion piece to *Daniel Blake* but a related film.

Were you always thinking that there would be two strands to this story?
No, I think what grew in Paul's mind was not only the level of exploitation for the individual worker but the consequences for family life and how everything refracts into personal relationships. The middle class talk about work-life balance: the working class are stuck with necessity.

Is this a new problem or is it an old one in a different guise?
It is only new in the sense that it's modern technology that's being used. The most sophisticated technology is in the driver's cab, dictating the routes, allowing the customer to know exactly where the parcel is that they've ordered and its estimated time of arrival. It will arrive, if it's a so-called 'preciser', within a certain hour. The consumer is sitting at home tracking this vehicle all

155

round the neighbourhood. It's an extraordinarily sophisticated piece of equipment with signals bouncing off a satellite somewhere. The result is one person knocking themselves out in a van going from pillar to post, from street to street, running to meet the demands of this equipment. The technology's new; the exploitation is as old as the hills.

How did you research the film?
Paul did most of the research, then we met some people together. Drivers were often quite reluctant to speak: they didn't want to risk their jobs. The depots were difficult places to get into. A very helpful man from a depot not too far away from where we were filming, who was the manager, gave us very precise advice in setting up the depot itself. The drivers in the film are almost all current drivers or ex-drivers. When we were doing those scenes, they knew the game; they knew the process, how it worked and the pressures of getting it done fast.

What struck you most from your research?
I think what is surprising is the hours that people have to work to make a decent living and the insecurity of their work. They're self-employed, and in theory it's their business, but if something goes wrong they take all the risk. Quite easily something can go wrong with the van and they get the equivalent of the sanctions on *Daniel Blake* if they're not there to deliver the service. Then they can lose a lot of money very, very quickly. For care workers like Abby it's the idea that they can be out doing visits for 12 hours but only get six or seven hours pay on the minimum wage.

Introduce us to the characters in *Sorry We Missed You*
Abby's a mother in a good marriage – she and Ricky are friends, there's affection between them, they trust each other and they both try to be good parents. Her problem is trying to care for her kids in the way she'd like to: she's working so hard that she's not there, so most of the time she's having to give instructions

to the kids over the phone. Of course, that tends to go wrong because kids are kids and she's not back till late at night. She's relying on buses, which are not that frequent, so a lot of time is spent hanging around at bus stops.

Who is her employer? Where does the pressure come from?

The employer is an agency. The care work is sub-contracted by the local council through an agency or a private healthcare company. They get the contract because they put in a low price. The authorities turn a blind eye to the fact that the low price is based on exploitation of the people doing the work. It's much harder for the people who are working for a private healthcare company to get organised into a union than workers who work for a local authority and have proper contracts.

Who is Ricky?

Ricky's a grafter, as he says himself. He was a building worker, probably served his time in one of the trades, probably plumbing or joinery. He was doing quite well – they'd saved enough for a deposit for a house. That coincided with the collapse of banks and building societies that left people like Ricky and Abby unable to get a mortgage. The building trade suffered, Ricky lost his job, and since then he's gone from job to job. He can turn his hand to anything. When we meet him, Ricky decides he wants to work as a delivery driver, where it seems that you can make a lot of money. The family's still in rented accommodation, they are not making enough to get out of debt, they've been existing hand to mouth for a few years, so this is a chance of working like hell for two or three years, get a deposit for a house, and then be able to live a normal life again. That's his plan. He's an engaging guy, very easy to get on with, and being from Manchester, he's a Manchester United fan, committed to making a success of his new job.

People in Ricky's position have to exploit themselves, no need for a foreman to crack the whip. They have to run themselves into the ground to make a decent income: the ideal situation for an employer.

What is Abby and Ricky's family set-up?
There are two kids. Seb is 16 and neither parent is there to keep an eye on him. He's going off the rails. He's got talents, artistic and creative, that they don't know about. What they do know is that he's bunking off school and he is getting into trouble. The sparks fly between father and son. Ricky is a bit old school – he just tells Seb what to do and expects him to do it and of course Seb doesn't. A confrontation is bound to happen.

Then there's Liza Jane. She's a very bright kid. She's the peacemaker in the family with a quirky sense of humour and red hair like her dad. She just wants everyone to be happy. She tries to keep the family together when it's all firing off in different directions.

How was the shoot in Newcastle?
As usual we shot it in sequence. The actors didn't know how it was going to end. Each episode was news to them. We rehearsed the family beforehand so that they had worked out something of the relationships between them. After that we shot it pretty quickly, in five-and-a-half weeks.

One of the main challenges was getting the parcel delivery depot right. We had to know the exact process and for everyone to know exactly what their job was and then we shot it like a documentary. We worked out who were going to be the people who received the parcels when they first came in, the sorters, who were the drivers bringing their vans in, what happened at each stage, the whole chain of events. Fergus and the design team did a brilliant job to enable that to happen.

Choreographing it was a challenge because it was a big, echoey working depot in an industrial estate. But the guys were terrific. They got stuck in and did it with a real relish. I hope that in the shots you can see that they know what they're doing, they're doing it fast, they're doing it under the eagle eye of the depot manager who cracks the whip. Everything had to be authentic. Nobody had to pretend.

We wanted the urban landscape of Newcastle to be present in the film but not so that it looked like tourist shots, not just to show off the city. I think you do get a sense of the landscape: you see the old terraces, you see the tower blocks and you see the city centre with its classic architecture.

What questions do you think are posed by *Sorry We Missed You*?

Is this system sustainable? Is it sustainable that we acquire our shopping through a man in a van knocking himself to pieces 14 hours a day? Is that, in the end, a better system than going to shops ourselves and talking to the shopkeeper? Do we really want a world in which people are working under such pressure, with the knock-on effects on their friends and their family and the narrowing of their lives? This is not the market economy failing – on the contrary, this is a logical development for the market, brought about by harsh competition to cut costs and maximise profit. The market is not interested in our quality of life. The market is interested in making money and the two are not compatible. The working poor, people like Ricky, Abby and their families, pay the price.

But in the end, all this counts for nothing unless the audience believes in the people on screen, cares for them, smiles with them and shares their troubles. It is their lived experiences, recognised as authentic, that should touch us.

Rebecca O'Brien
Producer

How did Sixteen Films get from *I, Daniel Blake* to *Sorry We Missed You*?

We didn't expect *I, Daniel Blake* to have the impact that it did, but with over 700 community screenings and a continued desire for people to talk about it, and to use the film as a fundraiser, it became a sort of totem. It was discussed in parliament and became a point of reference. People recognised themselves or people they knew in that film, and I think that a lot of people had been afraid to talk about the humiliation that the system put them through. It made it possible for people to feel that they weren't alone in their situation.

We did so many talks and discussions about *I, Daniel Blake*, met so many people who spoke of their experience that it gave us the impetus to make *Sorry We Missed You*. The conversations between Ken and Paul continued. Paul particularly got into the issues around insecure jobs and realised that there was another story to be told. What fitted so well was that whereas *I, Daniel Blake* deals with the world of benefits and welfare, *Sorry We Missed You* is about the world of work and the people Theresa May would call 'just about managing'. Then Paul wrote the characters of Ricky, Abby and their two kids.

Why did you choose to return to Newcastle to make it?

Newcastle is compact and comparatively easy to get around. That does make a difference: whereas in some cities you might take an hour to get from one place to another, in Newcastle that journey might take 15 or 20 minutes. Also, it's got a very strong cultural identity, while at the same time representing all of Britain in microcosm: it's a city with the highs and lows, good things and bad things about it that any British city might have. Because we got to know it through *Daniel Blake*, it made it much easier for us to come back here. We know the infrastructure and the people to work with and value the warmth of their welcome and enthusiasm.

Is *Sorry We Missed You* a specifically British story, or is it universal?

Britain is certainly not the only country that is instigating zero-hour contracts and operating systems like our care system. 'Precarious working' is to be found across the whole of Europe. We all buy things online, get them delivered by courier and everybody knows somebody who has been through the care system – a granny or a mother or a sister or a brother. We've seen it being both wonderful and terrible. We hope this film will show what both of those systems do to the children of overworked parents who don't have enough time for them.

What bearing does the global financial crisis of 2008 have on the story?

It's our backstory. I think in 2008 our couple might just have been able to get their mortgage together, but then banks and building societies collapsed and those who suffered were the most vulnerable. Where they might have had a mortgage, and might have had a place of their own, instead they're stuck living in temporary, rented accommodation. The other way it affected them is in the austerity programme. Abby and Ricky are both working, they should be fine, but they are underpaid. Ricky is desperate to break through and make something more for himself, so he can provide more for his family.

How has *Sorry We Missed You* been financed?

Once again it has been a co-production with the wonderful Why Not and Wild Bunch in France, who've both been incredibly supportive. BBC Films have come back on board again, as well as the BFI. Also, thanks to the BFI's Locked Box scheme we were able to recoup some money from *I, Daniel Blake* which has been invested in *Sorry We Missed You*. It's a great way to recycle lottery money and it means *I, Daniel Blake* has helped to pay for this film.

Is it becoming harder to get films like yours off the ground?

It is getting increasingly difficult to make independent British films. The audience has dwindled globally for independent films in recent years. That's another knock-on effect from the financial crisis, because after 2008 sales halved. People are far more risk-averse now. Films are having to be funded through all sorts of deals, equity breaks and patchwork funding. Luckily, with Why Not and Wild Bunch as partners, that's not been the case with our recent films: I'm in a very privileged position as a producer. It would be much more difficult to be starting out and doing the same thing.

You often work with the same crew. What does that bring to the production?

In terms of the look, the production design, the editing and the music, having those creative elements coming from the same sources does give a continuity. There's a shared vision of how the film should be that is consistent. Overall, I think it helps to have the look being similar because if you put Ken's films together it is one long story of our lives. I would like to think that in 200 years' time, if somebody wanted to have a look at the social history of our era, they might get something out of seeing 50 years' worth of Ken Loach's and the writers' films.

Cast

Kris Hitchen
Debbie Honeywood
Rhys Stone
Katie Proctor
Ross Brewster

Kris Hitchen
Ricky

Introduce us to Ricky...
Ricky's a hardworking bloke who just wants the best for his family. When we meet him it's a very tricky moment because he's just started out in a new business venture and there are things going on with his son Seb and with his family in general. He's always been the boss of the household and the main breadwinner – he always thinks he's got the answers. But now he's reached a point where he's starting to doubt himself and question whether the decisions he's made were the right ones for his family. It means he's coming apart at the seams a little because for the first time he's starting to ask himself what's it all about? What's the point?

What's Ricky's background?
He's done a lot of labouring jobs, semi-skilled building work, always worked in a team on building sites and done some landscape gardening. He can turn his hand to anything really on a building site just to make a wage. He's living in Newcastle – he came up here from Manchester after falling in love with Abby when he met her at a rave club and then they ended up having two children. A large part of his story is he's gone through the gamut of trying to get his own house and get a mortgage but obviously it's not worked out because of the Northern Rock collapse. When the delivery job idea comes along it's like this is his chance, a second bite of the apple. He's getting older so he's got to do it now he feels – a few years' hard graft to sort him and his family out.

What does he think he's getting into when Maloney, the depot manager, makes him the initial offer to work as a driver?

He kind of walks into it blindly because he's heard good stories from his mate who works at the same depot and he thinks that it's going to be a really good deal for him. With the work ethic he's got if he can get stuck in then he can generate the finances so that he can get his own house. Then he can finally get his family to move forward in the direction that he's always wanted for them.

As the story moves on, what are the pressures that start closing in on him?

It's the pressures of the job to start off with because he's constantly on the move, doesn't have a minute, has to deal with the traffic and has to deal with customers that, for want of a better word, are all dickheads. Then there's his son who's been getting in trouble at school. Seb has fallen in with the wrong crowd but Ricky's not home much so there's not much he can do about it. Also, his wife's working day has now become longer because she hasn't got a car to get to her care work jobs any more – and it's all connected because Ricky has sold the car in order to buy his van.

He's kind of created this clusterfuck without even meaning to create it. He's going into it with every good intention and it's just backfired. Now it's one situation after another and they just keep piling up. Ricky's attitude is that if there's a problem then if he works harder that will fix it. But it's not that simple. The system, in a way, has failed him and now it's failing his son too.

How did you get the role?

I began acting seriously when I turned 40. I'd almost paid my mortgage by then and I'd put my shift in doing 20 years as a self-employed plumber. I'd grafted for years to get my family into a position where I could do this and I asked my wife if it was okay – I had to have her blessing because she had to carry on working. She's ended up doing six days a week so that I could start doing this.

When this job came I had already seen it on Spotlight but they were looking for Newcastle actors only. Then out of the blue my agent got in touch with me and said they're looking for somebody from Manchester or Bolton. Well that's me: I live in Bolton but I'm from Manchester and I have the building background. I went to the auditions, I started chatting with Ken. I thought I blew it and then I got the call to go back. I just went all guns blazing – you only get one shot don't you? After that it was a really fast process. I got the phone call and I remember I had just been paid for some boilers as well. The last boilers I will ever fit, hopefully.

How have you found the shoot?
I'm really good friends with Steve [Evets, *Looking for Eric*]. He's been giving me support. He said, 'It's not going to be what you think it's going to be; it's nothing like any other job. You're going to have to think on your feet and deal with what comes at you. Just make sure you keep yourself fit, keep your wits about you, make sure you switch off and have time for yourself.' And that's exactly what I did.

Debbie Honeywood
Abby

Who is Abby?

Abby's a care worker. She's working every night apart from three nights a week, and she's struggling to get to work because her husband's sold her car. That's a big deal for a care worker living in a city. She's also trying to bring up a family. She's got two school-age kids, so she needs to be there. She's got that mum guilt. Put it all together and Abby's on the edge. She's constantly feeling guilty and she wants to do the best for everybody because she cares about everyone. She wants to look after the people she cares for in her job, although her priority is her kids and her husband, but she can't do it all.

How did Abby and Ricky end up in this situation?

Ten years ago the Northern Rock crash happened. Ricky was in the building trade. He got made redundant. They had got a mortgage promise on the house but that fell through. Then he just went from job to job. They were renting, moving from here to there. As for Abby, she's had this care job where you only get paid for your visits. Together they're just making ends meet but no more.

How did Abby and Ricky meet?

We met at a rave in Morecambe when we were both very young. I used to come down from Newcastle, he'd come from Manchester. One day I couldn't get back so he took me home in his battered old van, and he charmed his way in I think.

What is their relationship now?

I think it's like everyday life: in real-life relationships when you're working really hard, everything gets in the way. Everything else becomes a priority. When they do have time to even talk, let alone see one another? I don't know.

How did you come to be cast as Abby?

I'm a learning support assistant and I work in North Tyneside. When I was 40, I joined the agency NE1 4TV because on my bucket list I'd said I wanted to be on the telly. I got a background part on *Vera*. Then they asked me back and I got five words and that's it. I'm still on the list. Jobs come up all the time. This job came up and it described a woman in her 40s with two teenage kids who's softly spoken, tough, but people all like her. I showed my husband and he said, 'It sounds like you, go for it.' And as he did that, one of my best friends sent it to me at the same time!

I had to send a little video message on my phone to Ken and then I met him for a drink and then I had audition after audition. I didn't know what part I had until right at the very, very end. I have to say I swore several times when they told us it was one of the leads. I couldn't believe it. It was only a matter of weeks later that we were filming.

Did you meet people who work in care?

Yes, I went to a care home and I started helping out a little bit and asking the girls loads of questions. They sent me on a proper training course, so I trained with proper care workers so that I knew what to do, when and how. When I pushed the ladies that I met – it was all women – most of them have always done that job; it's a vocation, it's important to them. The women that I met are angels. They're like nurses that do everything and to be honest, at some points I was quite shocked at what they do for what they get paid. It was a massive learning curve for me. One thing I did realise is that in the film, when Ricky sells the car,

Abby's lost. Because she just hasn't got time to get from place to place and she's not being paid when she's travelling.

What was the shoot like for you?
Well, I'll be dead honest: first week I kept thinking, 'Is this really happening? Is this really me?' Second week, panic. Third week, 'Okay.' It's like a roller coaster. I cannot really compare it to *Vera* where I was just in the background washing some glass pipes in the forensic lab. It's been very emotional because I'm a mum, I've got a teenage older boy. When you're a mum and it's about a kid, I can feel it because I think, 'What if it was me?' My husband was made redundant after the Northern Rock crash. We had just bought a house. I work with kids whose parents have divorced: I've seen all sides of this situation.

How has it been working with Ken Loach?
It's very different because we don't get given everything up front. I get given a scene, I learn what I can, but as time goes on, the story, my bit of it, unfolds. It's all a surprise – sometimes quite literally, like when I've been caring for someone and they throw in a joke, and I wasn't expecting it. But when you understand the way that he [Ken Loach] works, and the way he teaches you to work, it's really amazing. I couldn't have had a better person to learn from. I don't know, this could be it for my acting. But I hope not. I'd love to do more.

Rhys Stone
Seb

Who are you playing?
I'm playing Seb Turner. I've got bright ideas that people don't understand. Especially my family, and so there's a bit of scuffling between the family, rows and stuff like that. His family don't understand what he's got in store and what he thinks about and all the things like that. He has this talent for spray painting, spraying graffiti. It shows off his creative side. But he's not been going to school so he can do the spray painting. And then there's a bit of arguing with the dad and stuff towards the end.

What's his relationship with Ricky, his dad?
Just always at each other's throats. I don't know the exact reason. All I know is that the dad doesn't see Seb's point of view. And it gets worse when his dad isn't there doing the delivery job. Then it's only him and Liza Jane left in the house by themselves – and Seb's always out. I mean, there's some good moments between the dad and Seb. Obviously they do love each other but they're just always at each other's throats.

How did you come to be in this film?
I worked with New Writing North. They helped me get this. I think Ken just came in to my school. I met him, shook his hand, said, 'Yalreet', and this and that. I went to another meeting and it was explaining certain things and then I went to the auditions. Every time I got there, I was giving it my best, and then somehow I got the main lead when I wasn't meant to get the main lead. I was meant to get like the secondary, but I got the main instead so I'm grateful for that, to be honest with you. That's a good step-up, isn't it?

How have you found the process, the way that Ken makes films?

It's good. It's more relaxing. There's less stress on the actors and stuff like that. Less stress on the crew and stuff. It's best to just give your best to be the best really, isn't it? Just to respect the man for what he does. Just pay attention and stuff like that. We did one scene and it was that close to home that I broke down. If it really connects with you that's a good experience to have. That was a big step-up for me.

Did you have to learn graffiti?

Yes, it's me doing it on screen. I had to do a couple of sessions practising how they do it properly, but I picked it up no problem. This guy called Jim, I think it is. He taught me how to do it. He taught me the difference between the cans and how good they are. Less pressurized. What nibs to use. How quick to do it to get your lines spot-on and things like that.

What's your relationship like now with Debbie, Kris and Katie?

It feels like we're a genuine family. It literally feels like we're a genuine family because I get along with Katie like she was my little sister. I get along with Kris, but there's less shouting! It's more like jokes and stuff like that, and me and Debbie are dead close as well.

What's it like to have to go through several weeks where you don't quite know where it's all going? You haven't seen the full script, so you don't quite know what's going to happen…

It's exciting. It gives you more energy to get up and learn what's happening on that day. Yes, you may be tired but just because you haven't seen the whole script that doesn't mean you can't pull it off. And you get some good surprises. There was one scene where we were all eating curry together and Kris [Hitchen] said a random line that just came out and it was funny. Obviously, it made me laugh. That's like a genuine emotion instead of being forced because if it was forced, it'd just sound stupid, wouldn't it?

Katie Proctor
Liza Jane

How did you come to be cast in *Sorry We Missed You*?
Well, my teacher came in to my Spanish lesson, and she was like, 'Are any girls in here acting?' Originally, I didn't put my hand up, but she knows me, and I've done school plays and stuff, so she was like, 'Come on, Katie. I know you like acting.' Then we went through and we were interviewed kind of, questions about me and Newcastle and stuff. Then they were interested in me and a few other girls, so we got took through to another audition, met Ken, and then that led to another and after about four auditions I was told I was in. I didn't know who Liza Jane was at the time.

Where were you when you found out that you got the part?
I was at gymnastics and my mum kept on phoning us. My ringtone is 'Hotline Bling', so we were joking and all my gymnastic friends were laughing because I was like dancing along to the tune. Then my coach said, 'You can go answer it if you want,' and I was like, 'It's my mum.' She says, 'You got the part,' and I was over the moon. I had only told one friend so I shouted over to her, 'I have the part.' She ran over and gave me a hug. Nobody else knew what I was talking about.

Had you heard of Ken Loach before this?
I've heard his name before but I hadn't seen any of his films because my mum said they were a bit too adult kind of for me – like more drama and stuff. My mum had seen them so she was telling us about them.

After you found out that you got the part, what were you told about Liza Jane?

I was just told she's a bit younger than you, not smaller but kind of a bit more babyish than I am personally, and just things like that. We're both 12 but her personality is a bit younger than me.

What is Liza Jane's life like?

I'd say she has a bit of a sad life but it's okay. She's got a roof over her head and she can always get food and stuff but it's just a bit sad sometimes. She has a good relationship with her mum and dad. She gets to go out in the van with her dad so that was a good laugh, driving around Newcastle with Kris [Hitchen, Ricky]. She sees less of him once he's started this job as a delivery driver and that probably makes her a bit more sad.

How have you found the process of filming with Ken?

He just wants you to be normal. When I'm on the camera, I don't think like, 'What would Katie do?' I think more like, 'I'm Liza Jane. What would I do?'

Ross Brewster
Maloney

Who is Maloney?

He's Ricky's boss at the delivery depot. And if I can use bad language, he's a bit of a prick. He's no nonsense, very straightforward. He makes it very clear what he expects and what he wants, which is for people to do the job and do the job well. If there's a problem, it's up to them to fix it, not to come to him with problems. That's not what he's there for. He's there to get the best people for the business. Then it's up to them to go and do deliveries on his company's behalf, so they can be number one in the country. He doesn't want to hear complaints. He has a 'If you don't want to be here, there's the door' kind of attitude. He's quite ruthless.

How did you come to be cast?

I've got absolutely no idea. I was signed up with this NE1 4TV agency and they sent out an email 'Looking for serving or retired police officers'. With me still being a serving cop, I was like, 'I can do that.' It didn't say what it was for. I replied to that just saying who I was, where I worked and what I had done within the service. After that I went to meet the casting director and that was how it all happened. When they offered me the job I was still thinking I was going to be playing a policeman. They said, 'You're going to play the part of the lead character's boss.' I was just like, 'What?' From doing absolutely nothing ever before, I'd landed this fantastic role of Maloney in this feature film, which I was just completely blown away by.

Why do you think they were looking for a police officer for the role?

Possibly they wanted somebody who has that capacity I guess internally to switch it on when they need to, to be that bit of a bastard, which is what Maloney is. 'My van's broken down.' 'Well, get it fixed.' 'I can't.' 'Well, get somebody else in. I'm not interested.' Sometimes you have to be a bit tough like that as a police officer.

What was it like on the shoot?

I'm well aware that there will be very well-established actors in the film industry who would give their right arm to work with Ken. I'm very lucky that he's picked me. As a director he's very comforting. Very patient. Very tolerant. Very appeasing. Somebody would come up with an idea, and he'd be like, 'That's a great idea, we'll do that.' Things would just veer off one way or the other and it would be like, 'Right, we're changing this.' Then he would be like, 'Okay, fine.' I don't have anything to compare it to but it was all very relaxed. I wasn't stressed, or worked up about it, or anything at all. It was fantastic: this guy was really brilliant.

What did you think of the gig economy beforehand and how has being involved in *Sorry We Missed You* changed your opinions?

I didn't have any idea about the gig economy, because I'm fortunate enough to be in a career where I'm employed on a full-time basis. I haven't had to have the worries, the fears, the concerns about being self-employed. From what I learned from the film, my God, not a chance. Not if you're going to have a boss like me, Jesus. Or if you don't have that support of a good employer, and a good welfare based system, and occupational health, and your counselling services and everything else that goes on with modern day life… to be on your own, standing on your own in that gig economy with a franchise with only you to care for yourself and you've got your family to provide for. I tell you what, I wouldn't want to do it.

Crew
Fergus Clegg
Ray Beckett
Kahleen Crawford
Eimhear McMahon

Fergus Clegg
Production Designer

What were the challenges in the script for production design?

The big thing is the scale of the warehouse because the question is where do you pitch it? You've got the mega companies like Amazon and the people that deal with all their products. So, where in the scale of distribution do you angle it? Rather than having something small scale, we wanted to pitch it in the middle somewhere – there are lots of companies around who do distribution for the big companies and we based it on their model. We got as much information as we could from their working methods in terms of the size of the units because they're all quite localized – a company may have two depots in Newcastle that cover half of the city each. They break it down into areas and then you'd have a warehouse of a certain size that serves that part of the city. We found that location.

What sort of research did you do?

We got some very useful help from a contact who came and helped us plan the mechanics of the operation. He said, 'A place like this, I'd have the vans in this arrangement and the process would be this.' He talked us through the practices and the layout of the space. We expected it to be much more high-tech because you look at images online of these big warehouses and there's lots of conveyors and that sort of stuff, but we're at a much lower level. It's much more manual. You're using trolleys perhaps to move things around but it is pretty much hard graft. It comes in on a big truck, comes off on these tall supermarket trolleys and then everything's man-handled. You see it broken down into postcode groups and then scanned.

How important is the scanner?

The scanner is the key because that's the technology that governs the whole process in terms of the postcodes, the tracking of the parcels, telling the driver what to do, telling him the route he has to go. That's the boss in the cab that's relaying all this information back to the head office. If they stop for a period, head office can say, 'Why has he stopped?' 'You're not on track to make that delivery.' If there's a before 10:00 or before 12:00 delivery, they know whether they're going to hit it or not, based on that scanner. It's just such an all-encompassing system.

How did you get hold of the scanners themselves?

To buy them new they're over £1,000 each and that's just the hardware. I found a company who are based near Liverpool who trade in second-hand gear. We hired some equipment from them, in terms of the large scanners that scan the items into the depot and the smaller hand-held devices that the drivers take with them everywhere. Those scanners... they're like a poisoned chalice. Without them, the drivers are lost. But with them, the scanner is their boss. They're notorious. You see stuff online of them freezing and having to be rebooted and that takes 20 minutes and in that time the drivers can't work. Technology is fine when it works, but obviously, when it goes down, everyone's stuffed, and the scanners mean the drivers are having to react to the demands set by head office.

Did your scanners actually work?

Yes! We had to make 2,000-plus parcels and boxes and then table them with barcodes and addresses that could be scanned by the handheld device scanners. We also had to get software especially written to enable the scanners we rented to read the barcodes we had especially printed and bleep (an important element of the incessant nature of the process) so that it felt like they were fully functioning and linked to a complete system. It's all part of Ken's drive for getting as close to reality as possible.

To what extent did you want Newcastle itself to be part of the film?

It was very much about Newcastle. *I, Daniel Blake* was also set in Newcastle but in that film we didn't see much of the city because lots of it was set at night. But it's a fantastic city to look at. When you come in on the train, you've got that fantastic vista of the bridges and St James's Park. The whole place is visual, and as Ricky is out in the van, we get a good picture of the city. Ken wanted to see the variety of deliveries that were taking place, from better-off households down to people who are at the bottom end, all ordering stuff online. It's about the effect it has on the city, the effect it has on the High Street, and the effect of all these vehicles on the roads. It has a profound impact – every time you go up to Newcastle you notice another shop has closed. It's just far easier to shop online. We're all guilty of it.

What look were you after for the film?

It's always following the Ken ethos of keeping it very subdued and letting the actors and the story take precedence. We're secondary, in terms of what we do: the main objective is just making the environment real. The Turner family home was quite a thing to find. It needed to be a rented property in an area full of other rented properties, so we went to Benwell, in the West End of Newcastle. We found landlords owning dozens of properties, renting them out to multiple occupancy tenants. It was once a tough area but now it's just about surviving. We found a type of property that is particular to Newcastle called a Tyneside flat. It's a Victorian maisonette that has two front doors side by side. One door goes to the ground floor, one goes up a staircase to the upper floor. That's something Ken settled on quite early: he thought that would be the typical dwelling for them. The landlords do the bare minimum in terms of upkeep so it's just one colour, the same carpet throughout, damp issues, maintenance always very poor really. The state of the flat is what drives Ricky to want to get out, take on the delivery work and try and get a better place.

How did you approach showing Seb's talent for graffiti?
We got involved with a local graffiti group initially, and then we found a local scenic artist who works on films and TV productions who also does some graffiti. We got him to train Rhys and the other three members of the gang: we took them from having no skills whatsoever to being able to feel confident and actually doing the sequence where they spray the graffiti on the gable wall. Luckily Rhys seemed to have a talent.

Ray Beckett
Sound Designer

Why did you want to work on *Sorry We Missed You*?
I always find Ken's films a wonderful challenge, because you know he's not going to ever be looping anything and there's a good chance that what you do on set is what's going to actually emerge through the cinema speakers. I get a lot of personal satisfaction from managing to pick up the challenge every day from his scenes. On his side, he also organises things so that I do have a fighting chance of getting the sound on location. No wind machines, cross dialogue or things like that. He knows that will get in the way of the sound.

What were the particular challenges of this script?
In the scene in the depot we've got all these big metal cages rolling around the floor. They were a nightmare generally, but there was one particular time when it was coming right across dialogue, one particular cage. I mentioned it to Ken and he completely changed the choreography of it so that we got the dialogue in the gaps. It still looks natural, but he manufactured a gap for the sound to come through.

What's your general approach working on Ken's films?
I mic all the actors like any mixer would. I have a personal mic on all of the participants, including some who only have a couple of lines, just to make sure that you've got full coverage. Then once I've got that, I have a microphone away, back from the action, that doesn't pick up any dialogue, it just picks up the general atmos of the place. Like going back to the depot scene in *Sorry We Missed You*, I had a mic way back over the whole scene.

194

It was a huge, cavernous, very live space. That paid off though, because generally it was getting the sound of the comings and goings of the vans and also the sounds of the trolleys and things mentioned above. But also when Maloney, the foreman, raises his voice, the whole space acted like an echo chamber. That worked out quite well.

A lot of the scenes are more intimate, in smaller rooms and flats. What are the challenges there?
In those scenarios, again, it's just a personal mic to get the detail of the voices, but if it is a very, very quiet scene, I like to use a boom mic over the top, just to give a warm sense of being right with them. In a way, some of those low dialogue scenes have been my favourite ones when I work with Ken, because when they work, they work really well. But then it's a high-risk strategy, because they're speaking so low and you've got so much gain on the mic that if a car goes by outside for instance it would sound like a tank. Again, Ken will organise things so we get a quiet street.

When you receive the script what stands out as challenges to be overcome?
With this script there were a lot of mobile phone calls. There aren't generally with Ken, but particularly in this one there are. It's very difficult to tap into a mobile phone call unless the person at the other end of the line is on speaker phone and you've got a mic there. One thing we had done in the past is have the person who's making the call have two mobiles. One goes to the actors on screen and the other one comes direct to me out of my phone. So it's two calls happening at the same time. That can work but it can be problematic for reasons beyond our control like the signal dropping out or outside noise. With this one we cheated a bit – we had the actor in a minivan close by so that I could get them on a radio mic. It was much more reliable and you can process that signal to sound like a phone later on.

Do you ever use sound to help facilitate Ken's notorious surprises?

Yes. There was one good scene on this film where the main character disappears into someone's garden to deliver a parcel. In the script there's a dog. It sounds like a rather large dog that barks at him in the garden and he rushes out in fear of his life. That turned out to be a recording of the dog we played through a very big loudspeaker in the garden. The first time we did it, as usual Ken didn't tell anybody that the speaker was in there. It really freaked Kris [Hitchen] out!

You've worked on many of Ken Loach's films. How have they evolved?

I think the films have become more specific because the actual argument has become more specific. His early films were more generalized about injustice, but because of what's been going on with austerity I think he and Paul have had to become much more specific – dot all the 'I's and cross all the 'T's about what's going on. I think that's probably why *I, Daniel Blake* was so successful, because people could really identify with it. People will identify with this film too. We all get deliveries at our front door. Hopefully, when the film comes out, it will make people understand how insecure these people's lives are made by the gig economy.

Kahleen Crawford
Casting Director

What was the casting process for *Sorry We Missed You*?
What Ken and I always do is we talk about the characters and what we're looking for in them. I then thought about people that I knew in Newcastle because of *I, Daniel Blake*, and we talked about names of people that we'd met before that we might meet again. I always contact the agents via Spotlight and put out a breakdown. Initially it was a very general call out for a man in an age range and woman in an age range, the area we were shooting, the accents we were looking for. Then Ken started meeting people, had ten minute chats and if they weren't a fit for the main characters we'd think of them for something down the line.

What is it you're looking for?
Initially it's a very personal gut reaction to people. It's where they're from, where they grew up and how their life has gone in terms of choices they've made and jobs they've done. We do it entirely by chatting to them, just getting a sense of people. Ken just draws things out of people. He and I are always very aligned on who we think is right for this or that character. Once we know that there's something about a person that's drawing us in for this or that character you get them in a room with another actor who's auditioning for a different part. That's when Ken starts giving them scenarios. They're very straightforward and they're nothing to do with the film. That's when you start to see people's instincts coming out and that's when we start to build a picture of what would it look like if someone played this or that part. It's a 100% different way to how you cast most TV or

films. We don't cast with a script, and we don't tell the actors much of the detail of a scene. They don't know the journey so they can't come prepared. It means when you're casting you're looking for a certain type of mind, a different skillset.

How did you find Kris Hitchen?

Kris was suggested by his agent although I believe he might have emailed himself too. Once we'd decided that Ricky could have come from Manchester, Ken went there, did his chats, did recalls and one of them was Kris. He was brilliant: he was the one out of several excellent actors that we felt was closest to the script as Paul had imagined it.

Then we started to do the casting in Newcastle with some people we'd already met and it just didn't quite come together. We didn't quite see a family emerging so we decided to meet some people who had not acted before. I contacted some people who had been carers, as well as a fantastic agency in Newcastle that really gets Ken's work and I said do you have anyone who's done some background work – maybe a line or two? They pulled out a few faces, one of whom was Debbie Honeywood. Ken had a chat with Debbie and she walked into the room saying, 'Why am I here? I don't understand what I am doing.' When she started doing the conversations her nerves disappeared, she was calm, clear and compassionate. She had all these things that we were looking for, it worked perfectly.

Is it harder casting teenagers and children than adults?

For Ken Loach? Yes. Teenagers are tricky because they're at a funny age. They become very self-conscious and they stop acting. Male teenagers are particularly difficult because they don't go to drama classes – there are far more boys doing sport and science and playing computer games than there are doing drama. When casting children you often come back to children who've been to theatre school. That's not what Ken wants. In this case, Newcastle has a small population, they had to have the right accent, they had to match the family and their voices had to make sense with each other – as well as being able to do the part.

We went to all the theatre groups we could find, we went to agents and asked them about kids, we contacted the high schools, the primary schools. We looked at maps and drew circles of areas in Newcastle to look at. We actively encouraged teachers to give us children who don't present themselves but have got the skills – the teachers are so important in this situation. Then we filmed a lot of chats, took their pictures and did the same thing we did for the adults. You're always trying to be as encouraging as possible. If we see any potential, child or adult, we give them another crack.

Eimhear McMahon
Line Producer

What was your role on *Sorry We Missed You*?
In a nutshell a Line Producer's job is to balance the creative ambition with the financial means. The Line Producer offers insightful budget directions and then ultimately the producer and director will decide what's best for the film. Because I was professionally 'born' at Sixteen Films I have a 360 degree perspective of Ken's whole process so that means that I'm very well informed to do my job, and to support Rebecca [O'Brien, Producer] when she's making key decisions.

How does this film compare to previous films you have worked on?
Ken, Paul and Rebecca have always set out to capture this completely realistic truth of the story that they're telling. My job coming on at a very early stage is to understand what Ken wants to achieve. I already know how he likes to work so then what's important is making sure the cast and crew understand the process. We're very lucky to have worked with a lot of HODs for a long time so they understand implicitly how he likes to operate. We shoot chronologically and we take our locations across a longer period in order to keep as much flexibility as we can in the telling of the story. Having made *I, Daniel Blake* in 2015 we already had all of our connections in Newcastle and all of Paul's research had been done there, so we had these contacts to work with from the outset. In some ways this did feel like a continuation of *I, Daniel Blake,* although there were some new faces too – we took on some local trainees and again we cast as many parts locally as we could in order to protect the sense of community that's very important to Ken's films.

Star trailers, dining buses, big 'Film unit' signs, hi–vis jackets etc are what people are accustomed to seeing on a normal shoot but that is absolutely what Ken recoils from. We try to operate in a sort of stealth mode throughout. It's much more economical from a budget point of view and it means you concentrate on your schedule; you're less likely to spill over. On this film Ken was sick on one day and we had to stand the crew down. But remarkably we didn't incur an extra day at the end. That demonstrates how in control of his process he is and how all the elements around him function to protect that control.

How early were you involved in the process?
Because I work in-house at Sixteen Films I was aware of the first whiff of an idea, if you like! I helped set Paul off on his early research: he goes away and is quiet for a while, you'll book little bits of travel for him and then one day he'll turn up with a notes document and very quickly after that there'll be a script. So I was aware loosely what the story would be but until I get a script we don't start work on it. It's actually Ken really who does the first schedule and he maintains that schedule throughout. Obviously it's scheduled chronologically, although some scenes can jump out of chronology if it doesn't impact other key parts of the narrative. Then off the back of that schedule I'll get my teeth stuck into a budget. With Rebecca, we'll set the budget level and talk through numbers of supporting artists, the shape of the locations, what's doable and what isn't – there's a lot of driving in *Sorry We Missed You*, for example, and that can take time and be cumbersome. As it happened, we just shot it handheld in the front of the van and Ken was strapped in the back.

What were the particular challenges of this film from your point of view?
It was mostly to do with the setting up of the depot. We had to look for a unit that was free far in advance, and in a suitable environment, but also one that they would keep available for

us, because there's such a high turnover of rentals in that area. Then it was making it look like a real depot: I think in the end everyone agreed we massively succeeded.

Another challenge was working with some people who have difficult home lives or are from disadvantaged backgrounds. You just need to be sensitive to the fact that there are cast members who are not experienced actors.

Then, finally, there are the things you just can't predict. We had a 75mm Master Prime lens nicked off the back of a FedEx delivery van. Talk about life imitating art – without knowing the context of a) what had been stolen and b) that we were making a film – the FedEx representative said to me, 'Don't worry, the driver is an owner driver and therefore it's fully his responsibility.' It just highlighted what a dire situation a lot of these drivers are in with zero protection.

How did this story affect you?

One of the most powerful things for me in the film is that it's not a family in destitution – I think they represent a fairly average family in the UK. I actually found it much more emotional than *I, Daniel Blake* because of the journey that the family goes on. The performances are fantastic and I feel like we all know families who are in this predicament – they're just a couple of pay cheques away from being in a very dire situation.

Let There Be Light
Paul Laverty & Ken Loach

I met Dave on the 29th of July 2017 inside Tesco's cafeteria in Dunfermline, Scotland, while we were wrestling with a film idea that eventually became *Sorry We Missed You*. Dave drove a white van, and had worked for several courier companies, including Amazon.

Typically he would get up at 4.45am. He would leave home at 5am. He would get into a holding car park at the giant warehouse and try and make sure he would be there early enough to get a good position so he wouldn't be crowded out on the first wave of 'loading up' by the other 400 drivers.

In the car park he was not allowed to mingle with the other drivers. The company said it was for 'safety reasons' but Dave had other ideas. 'Best to keep us separate, easier to control us.'

Dave would often wait up to two hours before loading his van. Only then would his official working day begin. Each day would be different but sometimes he would deliver over 200 parcels at the busiest times. His record was 218.

The handheld device, HHD, nicknamed 'a gun', was his constant companion. It scanned every parcel, photographed each item if left in a place of safety as instructed by the customer, received calls and messages, and by GPS monitored every step Dave took. It bleeped if he was outside his van for more than two minutes. It worked out a route, and gave an estimated time of arrival (ETA), and also orders for parcels that had to be delivered within a window of one hour – known as 'precisers' – sometimes causing havoc, zig-zagging his route, to make the deadline.

Such were the relentless demands of his HHD, he would

often jog to make sure the parcel was scanned and delivered to the client on time.

Dave carried a plastic bottle in his van to piss in.

On exceptional occasions when lady luck went his way he could finish his work in the early afternoon, but usually he finished between 7pm and 8pm, then a drive of fifty minutes home.

Dave worked six days a week. He had one day off per week, but many times the day off would change by text at short notice according to the needs of the company. He had no holidays, no sick pay.

Dave had a pale-grey complexion and sunken eyes.

Algorithm, creativity, imagination and technology had pushed Dave to the extreme limits of physical and mental endurance.

He felt dizzy one day and nearly passed out driving.

His body and mind worked to meet the relentless deadline, and he spoke like a man scooped out from the inside. 'I feel like a tube of toothpaste.'

In law, Dave was self-employed, in control, and master of his own business. In reality, he was a man on the brink.

Two days before meeting Dave, on the 27th of July 2017, there was a fluctuation of share prices in Amazon which meant that its owner, Mr Jeff Bezos, became the richest man in the world with a fortune of just over 90 billion dollars.

But it took the newspapers a few days to catch up. Over the table I passed Dave that day's newspaper with the smiling photo of Mr Jeff Bezos.

Dave was silent for a long time as he stared at the image and digested the contents.

Mr Bezos named his company Amazon after the river because it began with A, the first letter in the alphabet.

How many Daves were there, drip by drip, around the world, white vans on roadways like streams, swelling into 'Fulfilment Centres' and finally profit thundering at breakneck speed in unimaginable quantities into the wide open arms of Mr Bezos at the far far far end of the tens of millions of handheld devices?

A year later Mr Bezos became the first 'centi–billionaire' with a fortune of over 150 billion, putting him ahead of the GDP of some 98 countries.

Dave cut a forlorn figure as he left the cafeteria.

Two sides of the same coin; unimaginable inequality and systematic exploitation of labour. Perhaps the greatest challenge of our times alongside climate change.

I followed Dave five minutes later down the same road which brought me close to a modest stone house. It was the original home of Andrew Carnegie who left Dunfermline as an impoverished child and went on to make his fortune in the States. It now serves as a museum.

Carnegie sold his Pittsburgh Steel Company in 1901 to JP Morgan for 303,450,000 dollars making him the richest man of his times.

Carnegie bought a 64–room mansion in New York, and Skibo Castle, part of a 22,000 acre estate in the Scottish Highlands.

There was a great deal of information on Carnegie's philanthropic work over the last 18 years of his life, during which he gave away over 90 percent of his fortune and built over 3,000 libraries around the world and of course the Carnegie Hall in New York.

Unsurprisingly I don't recall much information on the Homestead Strike in one of his factories in Pennsylvania. This was an infamous bloody confrontation with the Amalgamated Association of Iron and Steel Workers of the United States (generally seen as very moderate union at the time) in 1892 lasting over 143 days. Carnegie's partner Henry Clay Frick, virulently anti-union, led the action while Carnegie was in Scotland. Carnegie always tried to minimise his role in this battle though clearly stating to Frick before leaving that they should not hesitate to close down the factory if the workers didn't agree to their changes. He wrote to Frick, 'We all approve of anything you do, not stopping short of approval of a contest. We are with you to the end.' Frick hired the infamous Pinkerton National Detective Agency, armed agents and well-known strike breakers, to protect scab labour mostly made up of immigrant workers. In the violence seven workers were killed, including three Pinkertons, and hundreds were injured. The State sent in paramilitaries. The union was crushed. Profits gushed in as business as usual was restored.

The photos of the factories are stunning and set the imagination flying; the furnaces, molten flames, and great coke ovens. Thousands of men packed in together in one dramatic setting. There were many horrific accidents and explosions. One 'puddler' wrote of his work with a 25 pound spoon stirring the fiery liquid. 'I am like some frantic baker in the inferno kneading a batch of iron bread for the devil's breakfast.' Les Standiford, from whom I got the above quote, wrote that it was generally accepted that a 40-year-old man in this work was 'all worn out'.

Mr Carnegie lived until he was 83. As he opened a stunning sandstone library in the United States he addressed those present. 'Believe me, fellow workmen, the interests of capital and labour are one.'

Mr Bezos doesn't need the Pinkertons.

Amazon hires employee relations managers that, according to an advert, 'must have at least seven years direct experience in... union avoidance work, or labour law with an emphasis on union avoidance'.

Amazon doesn't need the overseer, it has the algorithm and handheld device.

We are blind to an army of Daves, hundreds of thousands of white van drivers weaving in among us, and knocking politely on our doors.

They don't get scalded by liquid steel, but I do wonder how many have crashed after hours of exhaustion, (I did hear from a bone fide journalist that an Amazon transport manager had resigned at the number of road accidents but I was never able to confirm this allegation. But I do wonder when the Government will do some rigorous research.)

Carnegie would have marvelled at present-day lawyers and publicists, masters of disguise.

Bogus self-employment transfers risk from the company to the worker, hidden behind new words like 'onboarding' instead of hiring, and 'fees' paid instead of a wage.

Technology, finance, contract, language, all genuflect before these giant corporations. Public perception is carefully sculpted; the cult of wealth and philanthropy dance as one.

Exploitation sold as freedom.

William Blake warned us of 'the mind-forg'd manacles'.

Technology changes, but not the age-old questions.

The central library in Edinburgh was built by Carnegie too. Cut into the sandstone above the main door are the words: 'LET THERE BE LIGHT'.

Paul Laverty
Edinburgh, 18th January 2019

An afterthought by Ken Loach:

The degree of exploitation that Paul describes is not an aberration. It is not a mark of capitalism's failure but of its inexorable development. Harsh competition between giant corporations in a global market forces them to cut labour costs, discipline their workers and instruct their politicians to fix the rules in their favour.

Blake's 'mind-forg'd manacles' keep us shackled to an idea of a world in which the few have wealth and power and the many suffer the consequences. While the Left sing the Internationale, the Right promote a narrow nationalism while acting on an international scale.

The questions are always the same. How do we fight back? What is our strategic aim? What are our strengths?

Given the increasing dangers of the environment, we do not have the luxury of time. We used to think that if we lose one battle, we might win the next. We know now that the present danger of climate change is urgent. Can it be alleviated without a planned economy? The evidence suggests that the answer is no.

The problems we face are not new: poverty, exploitation, alienation, a lack of political power and, to a large extent, an absence of political leadership. The answers are written in history if only we open our eyes to see them. Peaceful co-existence with capitalism does not work – social democracy has failed and the parties that promoted it have all but disappeared.

Our task has surely to be directed toward organization in the workplace and in communities, defending what remains of our public services, with strong unions and political parties. Then leadership becomes critical. There must be an understanding of, and commitment to, the independent interests of the working class. That means developing economies based on common ownership and democratic control, with the ability to plan the careful use of the earth's resources.

Easy to write, but a herculean task.

Answers on a postcard please...

'Let There Be Light' first appeared in the collection *A Vision for Europe* edited by David Adler and Rosemary Bechler, published by Eris, London 2019.

Film Credits

CAST

Ricky	KRIS HITCHEN
Abby	DEBBIE HONEYWOOD
Seb	RHYS STONE
Liza Jane	KATIE PROCTOR
Maloney	ROSS BREWSTER
Henry	CHARLIE RICHMOND
Freddie	JULIAN IONS
Rosie	SHEILA DUNKERLEY
Robert	MAXIE PETERS
Ben	CHRISTOPHER JOHN SLATER
Mollie	HEATHER WOOD
Harpoon	ALBERTO DUMBA
Roz	NATALIA STONEBANKS
Dodge	JORDAN COLLARD
Magpie	DAVE TURNER
Policeman	STEPHEN CLEGG
Council Worker	DARREN JONES
Traffic Warden	NIKKI MARSHALL
Man with drip	MIKE MILLIGAN
Snapchat Friend	GRACE BROWN
Neighbour	STEVE HOGG
Woman at door	MARY SHEARER
Woman at the bus stop	CHRISTINE BECK
Man who won't show ID	MICKY MCGREGOR
Janitor	GAVIN WEBSTER
Attackers	ALEX HOUSTON
	JORDAN SAWYER
	RUSSELL JONES
Corridor Nurse	VICKY HALL

Drivers	ANDY KIDD
	LES HALL
	CAROL ANDERTON
	CAROLINE LITTLEFAIR
	TIM MCGUIRE
	JOHN TORRANCE
	ANTHONY CUMMINGS
	ALFIE DOBSON
	NORMAN SANSOM
	ANTHONY HOGG
Packers	PAUL WOODHEAD
	RANDOLPH PAUL
	ROB KIRTLEY
	JACK HAMILTON
	ANDREA JOHNSON
Office Staff	ANITA SARKER
	HARRIET GHOST
Stunt Performers	JAMIE EDGELL
	ANDY GODBOLD
	CHRIS MORRISON
	SEON ROGERS

AND

Olivia Cave, Amy Dodd, Kay Gilchrist-Ward,
Shasimo Muwande, Watida Muwande,
Watifadza Muwande, Millie Preen, Susan Robinson,
Ebony Weatherson, Millie Welsh, Teagan Williams, Angus Wright

CREW

DIRECTOR	Ken Loach
PRODUCER	Rebecca O'Brien
SCREENPLAY	Paul Laverty
EXECUTIVE PRODUCERS	Pascal Caucheteux
	Grégoire Sorlat
	Vincent Maraval
PRODUCTION DESIGNER	Fergus Clegg
PHOTOGRAPHY	Robbie Ryan
RECORDIST	Ray Beckett
SOUND EDITOR	Kevin Brazier
CASTING	Kahleen Crawford
COSTUME DESIGNER	Joanne Slater
ASSISTANT DIRECTOR	David Gilchrist
LINE PRODUCER	Eimhear McMahon
EDITOR	Jonathan Morris
MUSIC	George Fenton
Stunt Co-Ordinator	PAUL HEASMAN
Assistant Producer	JACK THOMAS-O'BRIEN
Production Co-ordinator	SHONA MACKENZIE
ScreenSkills Production Trainee	CHARLES FORD ADAMS
Director's Assistant	EMMA LAWSON
2nd Assistant Director	JAMIE HAMER
3rd Assistant Director	LA'TOYAH MCDONALD
Floor Runner	CALLUM JOHNSON
Script Supervisor	SUSANNA LENTON
Script Consultant	ROGER SMITH
Stills Photographer	JOSS BARRATT
Titles Design	MARTIN BUTTERWORTH
	CREATIVE PARTNERSHIP
Casting Associate	CAROLINE STEWART
Casting Assistant	MARIANNE MCIVOR
Focus Puller	ANDREW O'REILLY
Clapper Loaders	THIBAULT WALCKIERS
	ALEXANDER CABANNE

ScreenSkills Camera Trainee	NATALIE LONGSTAFF
Daily Grip	BOB DIXON
Location Manager	MARK GALES
Unit Manager	DAVE GALES
Creative Skillset Location Trainee	STUART WHARTON
Boom Operator	CONOR MCALEESE
Sound Trainee	ADAM YOUNG
Gaffer	LAURENT VAN EIJS
Electricians	FRANCOIS TIBERGHIEN
	ANTOINE DOYEN
Dailies	VINNY COWPER
	DAVID DALTON
	DAVID FARMER
	ROSS SHANKLAND
Prop Buyer	CRAIG MENZIES
Art Director	JULIE ANN HORAN
Assistant Art Director	ZOE ROBINSON
Art Department Assistant	RUBY ALEXANDRA HIRST
Prop Master	PAUL CAMPBELL
Dressing Props	ANDREW PRATT
	JAMES KILLEN
Standby Props	CAMPBELL MITCHELL
Prop Dailies	BRIAN WATSON
	BOB MOFFATT
Artist in Residence	AIDAN DOYLE
Painters	BOBBY GEE
	LEO MORAN
Carpenters	GEORGE WRIGHT
	GLENN THEWLIS
Riggers	DW SCAFFOLDING
Make-up and Hair Designer	ANITA BROLLY
Make-up Dailies	FIONA WALSH
	LAURA TALLENTIRE
Wardrobe Supervisor	SARAH KATE GOODWIN
Wardrobe Standby	FIONA GREAVES

Production Accountant	HABIB RAHMAN
Assistant Production Accountant	ZEESHAN TAHIR
Catering	SCREEN CUISINE:
	PAUL BRUCE
	MARK NYE
	LLOYD HUMPHREY
	JAMES HARKIN
Security	TITAN SECURITY
Transport	RON ROBSON
	KEVIN WILSON
	CLÉMENT DAMAS
	DIEGO DUTORDOIR
Assistant Editor	RACHEL DURANCE
Post Production Staff	MERRYN BISHOP
	ANDY NICHOLSON
Cutting Room	DIRECTORS' CUT
Effects Editor	ROBERT BRAZIER
Dialogue Editor	BEN BRAZIER
Foley	IAN WILKINSON
	ROWENA WILKINSON
	MIKE GRIMES
For Molinare, Colourist	GARETH SPENSLEY
Online Editor	JUSTIN TILLETT
DI Producers	JOANNA BURT, ALAN PRITT
Lighting & Camera Equipment	EYE-LITE BRUSSELS, SET BASIX
Film Stock	KODAK
For Dejonghe Film Post Production	DIRK DEJONGHE
	HANNES BRUNEEL
Neg Cutter	STEVE FARMAN
Post Production Script	SAPEX SCRIPTS
Re-recording Mixers	IAN TAPP
	ANDREW CALLER
Sound Mix Technician	ASHLEIGH DAVIES
Re-recording Operations Manager	JAMES DOYLE
Recorded and mixed	
at Angel Studios by	JEREMY MURPHY
Pro Tools Recordist	LAURA BECK
Music Associate	SAMUEL PEGG

SCORE MUSICIANS   *Violins:* Tom Pigott-Smith
                                  Clio Gould
                                  Marianne Haynes
                                  Gabrielle Lester
                                  Rita Manning
                                  Chris Tombling
                                  Violas: Roger Chase
                                  Lydia Lowndes-Northcott
                                  Fiona Winning
                                  Celli: Caroline Dearnley
                                  Martin Loveday
                                  Frank Schaefer
                                  Double Basses: Chris Laurence
                                  Richard Pryce

KNOW HOW
Performed by Young MC
Licensed courtesy of Concord Music Group Inc.
Written by Matt William Dike; Isaac Lee Hayes;
John Wylie King; Michael Simpson; Marvin Young
Published by Universal Music Publishing Ltd.
On behalf of Irving Music, Inc.
and Universal/MCA Music Ltd. On behalf of Universal Music Corp.,
BMG Rights Management UK Ltd., Concord Music Group Inc.
Archive Courtesy of
SKY VISION

THANK YOU
Sergio Bollain; Helena Perez Minguez; Ewa Jasiewicz;
Jason Moyer-Lee; Maggie Dewhurst & the I.W.G.B; Joe Shaw;
Guy Millar; Norrie Buchan; Barry Scade;
Nigel Mackay & Michael Newman at Leigh Day; Peter Jamieson;
Mick Rix, Andrew Aldwinkle, Calne Waterson & Dave Day at the GMB;
John McGowan & the Social Workers Union;
Karen Head, Kay Pearson and staff at Barnardo's Pathways Service Falkirk;
Clare Daly; Scottish Centre for Conflict Resolution;
Beth McLeod; Pauline Nicol-Bowie;
Mike Dailly and Staff at the Govan Law Centre; Alan McIntosh;
Dave & Emma Adams; Shelly Marshall;
Donna Aldridge; Dave Cameron; Matthew Egan at Unison;
Alice Martin & Annie Quick at the New Economics Foundation;
Sophie Sherratt; Katie Broon; Tony Lawrence; Paul Carnie;
Acorn Newcastle; Alex Hamilton

Thanks to the drivers and carers who shared information with us
but did not want to give their names.

Newcastle Arts Centre; Staff at the County Hotel;
Northern Film and Media; Mark Stavers; Vicky Hall; Arriva;
Sandy Duff at Co Musica; Jeremy Dyson; Matthew De Vere; Alan Neal;
Julie Bemment; Holly Knox at Excelsior Academy; Emily Wiseman;
Kerrie Palma at Sacred Heart High School;
Michael Bell at Patchwork Project; Brunswick Methodist Church;
The Staff of Riverside Community Health Project;
Northumbria University Clinical Skills Centre; Newcastle Labour Club;
St Dominic's Club Byker; The Marin Luther Church;
Benwell Turkish Community Centre;
and Puppy the three-legged dog.

Insurance	MEDIA INSURANCE BROKERS
Script Clearances	SEELING LAFFERTY
Legal	STEPHEN GROSZ
	TAMSIN ALLEN
	BINDMANS LLP
Auditors	MALDE & CO
For Why Not Productions	LAURENT BERTHOU
	MARTINE CASSINELLI
	NICOLAS LIVECCHI
	STEVEN MARTIN
	BEATRICE MAUDUIT
	BENJAMIN TOUSSAINT
	ROSA ATTAB
For Wild Bunch	EVA DIEDERIX
	EMMANUELLE CASTRO
For Les Films du Fleuve	DELPHINE TOMSON
	ADRIENNE D'ANNA
	PHILIPPE TOUSSAINT
For BFI	BEN ROBERTS
	FIONA MORHAM
	IAN KIRK
	CLARE COULTER
For BBC Films	ROSE GARNETT
	MICHAEL WOOD
	GERALDINE ATLEE
	LIVY SANDLER
	EMMA HEWITT
	RUTH SANDERS

PRODUCED WITH THE SUPPORT OF

Brahim Chioua, Valérie Boyer, Bertrand Hassini-Bonnette,
Didier Lupfer, Laurent Hassid, Kristina Zimmermann, Anne Flamant,
Jean Labadie Philippe Logie, VOO and BE TV, Isabelle Molhant,
the Tax Shelter of the Belgian Federal Government, Casa Kafka Pictures,
Casa Kafka Pictures Movie Tax Shelter empowered by Belfius.

Collection Agent   FREEWAY CAM B.V
International Sales   WILD BUNCH S.A

A UK / French / Belgian Co-Production under the
European Convention on Cinematographic Co-Production

Filmed on location in Newcastle Upon Tyne.

Made with the support of the BFI's Film Fund

A special thanks to Artist-in-Residence Aidan Doyle who nourished us all throughout the shoot. His generous eye captured the teamwork required to make a film.